Pearson Edexcel GCSE (9–1) French Writing

Danièle Bourdais
and Geneviève Talon

Published by Pearson Education Limited, 80 Strand, London, WC2R ORL.

www.pearsonschoolsandfecolleges.co.uk

Copies of official specifications for all Pearson qualifications may be found on the website: qualifications.pearson.com

Produced by Out of House Publishing
Typeset by Newgen KnowledgeWorks Pvt. Ltd., Chennai, India

First published 2018

21 20 19 18
10 9 8 7 6 5 4 3 2 1

British Library Cataloguing in Publication Data
A catalogue record for this book is available from the British Library

ISBN 978 1292 24582 9

Printed in Slovakia by Neografia

Notes from the publisher

1. While the publishers have made every attempt to ensure that advice on the qualifications and its assessment is accurate, the official specification and associated guidance materials are the only authoritative source of information and should always be referred to for definitive guidance. Pearson examiners have not contributed to any sections in this resource relevant to examination papers for which they have responsibility.
2. Pearson has robust editorial processes, including answer and fact checks, to ensure the accuracy of the content in this publication, and every effort is made to ensure this publication is free of errors. We are, however, only human, and occasionally errors do occur. Pearson is not liable for any misunderstandings that arise as a result of errors in this publication, but it is our priority to ensure that the content is accurate. If you spot an error, please do contact us at resourcescorrections@pearson.com so we can make sure it is corrected.

This workbook has been developed using the Pearson Progression Map and Scale for French.

To find out more about the Progression Scale for French and to see how it relates to indicative GCSE 9–1 grades go to www.pearsonschools.co.uk/ProgressionServices

Helping you to formulate grade predictions, apply interventions and track progress.

Any reference to indicative grades in the Pearson Target Workbooks and Pearson Progression Services is not to be used as an accurate indicator of how a student will be awarded a grade for their GCSE exams.

You have told us that mapping the Steps from the Pearson Progression Maps to indicative grades will make it simpler for you to accumulate the evidence to formulate your own grade predictions, apply any interventions and track student progress. We're really excited about this work and its potential for helping teachers and students. It is, however, important to understand that this mapping is for guidance only to support teachers' own predictions of progress and is not an accurate predictor of grades.

Our Pearson Progression Scale is criterion referenced. If a student can perform a task or demonstrate a skill, we say they are working at a certain Step according to the criteria. Teachers can mark assessments and issue results with reference to these criteria which do not depend on the wider cohort in any given year. For GCSE exams however, all Awarding Organisations set the grade boundaries with reference to the strength of the cohort in any given year. For more information about how this works please visit: https://qualifications. pearson.com/en/support/support-topics/results-certification/understanding-marks-and-grades.html/Teacher

Contents

Get started

1 Giving clear information and opinions

This unit will help you to convey clear information and opinions. The skills you will build are to:

- clearly address all the bullet points in the question
- express opinions clearly
- only use language that you know to be correct.

In the exam, you will be asked to tackle a writing task such as the one below. This unit will prepare you to plan and write your own response to this question, giving clear information and opinions.

Exam-style question

Les relations personnelles

Un forum francophone sur les relations personnelles pose la question «Qui aimes-tu bien et pourquoi?»

Écris un message pour le forum. Tu **dois** faire référence aux points suivants:

- les personnes que tu aimes bien
- les qualités personnelles de ces personnes
- ton/ta meilleur(e) ami(e) à l'école primaire
- les personnes que tu vas voir ce week-end.

Écris 80–90 mots environ **en français**. **(20 marks)**

The three key questions in the **skills boosts** will help you to give clear information and opinions.

How do I clearly address all the bullet points in the question?

How do I express opinions clearly?

How do I only use language that I know to be correct?

Look at the sample student answer on the next page.

Get started

Read one student's answer to the exam-style question on page 1.

Je m'entends bien avec mon frère, Thomas. On se chamaille quelquefois mais par contre, si j'ai des problèmes, je peux me confier à lui. Au collège, ma meilleure copine s'appelle Chloé. Elle est intelligente mais pas prétentieuse. En plus, elle est très généreuse et, en particulier, elle m'aide quand on fait nos devoirs. Chloé et moi, on s'est connues à l'école primaire. En fait, elle était timide quand elle était petite. Ensuite, on a commencé le collège ensemble et on est restées amies. D'ailleurs, ce week-end, je vais retrouver Chloé en ville et on va voir un feu d'artifice.

Lisa

1. Has Lisa addressed all the bullet points in the question? Circle the relevant words or phrases in the text and number them 1–4.

   1 les personnes que tu aimes bien

   2 les qualités personnelles de ces personnes

   3 ton/ta meilleur(e) ami(e) à l'école primaire

   4 les personnes que tu vas voir ce week-end

2. In the exam, you are expected to make references to the past (using the perfect and/or imperfect tenses) and the future. Write the main tense(s) you will need next to each bullet point.

   - les personnes que tu aimes bien ....
   - les qualités personnelles de ces personnes ....
   - ton/ta meilleur(e) ami(e) à l'école primaire ....
   - les personnes que tu vas voir ce week-end ....

3. Lisa uses connectives to help convey how she feels about Thomas and Chloé. Complete the following two steps for a–e below.

   i Find and note down the French equivalent for these words and phrases.

   ii Underline the one that expresses a contrast.

   a but on the other hand, ...

   b moreover, ...

   c in particular, ...

   d in fact / as a matter of fact, ...

   e besides / as it happens, ...

How do I clearly address all the bullet points in the question?

Make sure that you:

- respond to all the bullet points and keep the information relevant
- choose the right tenses and the right verb forms to keep your message clear.

① Here is Jack's answer to the exam-style question on page 1.

a Highlight the relevant sections in his text and draw lines to link them with the corresponding bullet points on the right.

b Circle any bullet point(s) that he hasn't addressed in his answer.

c Cross out ~~cat~~ any irrelevant information in his answer.

J'aime bien mon beau-père, Simon, parce qu'il a le sens de l'humour. On va au foot ensemble et même quand notre équipe perd, il est cool et il voit le bon côté des choses. Par contre, je ne m'entends pas du tout avec ma belle-mère, qui est toujours pessimiste. Mon meilleur copain s'appelle Dylan. On s'est rencontrés parce qu'on faisait du judo ensemble et maintenant on est dans la même classe au collège. Dylan est toujours de bonne humeur et il me fait rire. On va souvent au skatepark le week-end.

- les personnes que tu aimes bien
- les qualités personnelles de ces personnes
- ton/ta meilleur(e) ami(e) à l'école primaire
- les personnes que tu vas voir ce week-end

② You will have to write about the past as well as the future, using correct verb forms and time markers to make your meaning completely clear.

Correct tenses are one of the most important skills for the Higher Writing exam. Revise main tense forms of key verbs such as *avoir*, *être*, *faire*, *aller*, …

a The sentence beginnings below tell us when an action is taking place. Draw lines to match each one with a sentence ending.

b Label each full sentence **Pr** (present), **Pa** (past – the perfect and/or the imperfect) or **F** (future).

A La semaine dernière,	**a** avec mes frères et sœurs.	
B Quand j'ai rencontré Maxime,	**b** je vais rendre visite à ma tante préférée.	
C Le week-end prochain,	**c** nous allons faire du camping samedi prochain.	
D S'il fait beau,	**d** nous étions à l'école primaire et j'avais six ans.	
E En général, je m'entends bien	**e** mes grands-parents faisaient beaucoup de sport.	
F Quand ils étaient plus jeunes,	**f** nous sommes allés au cirque.	

2 How do I express opinions clearly?

Express your opinions clearly by putting across a coherent viewpoint. Using a few well-chosen connectives (linking words) will help you do that.

1 Read this student's paragraph about an evening out in town. The writer has given only vague opinions and sometimes no opinion at all.

a Read the more developed opinions **A–E** and translate them into English on paper.

b Write the letter of each opinion in the box where it fits best in the text.

En septembre, il y a un festival dans ma ville. C'est intéressant. (1) ☐ Samedi, je suis sorti avec mon copain Kemal. Nous avons regardé un spectacle de cirque. C'était super. (2) ☐ On a aussi écouté un concert de rock fusion par Daft Punk. C'était bien. (3) ☐ Après, j'ai emmené Kemal au café et nous avons retrouvé ma copine Carla. C'était sympa. (4) ☐ Nous avons pris le bus à minuit et nous sommes rentrés. (5) ☐

A D'ailleurs, j'ai acheté le CD.

B Franchement, nous étions contents mais très fatigués.

C Les acrobates en particulier étaient formidables.

D En plus, il y avait une bonne ambiance.

E En fait, c'est la meilleure période pour visiter la ville.

The phrase *d'ailleurs* introduces a new example that reinforces the point you are making.

Useful connectives:
d'ailleurs – besides / as it happens
franchement – to be frank
en particulier – in particular
en plus – moreover
en fait – in fact

2 Connectives can be used to introduce a contrasting opinion as well as a similar one. In these sentences, circle the correct connective according to the meaning.

More connectives:
malheureusement – unfortunately
par contre – by contrast
en revanche – by contrast
cependant – however
d'un autre côté – on the other hand

a Le concert était super. **En particulier, / Cependant,** les billets étaient très chers.

b J'ai bien aimé la patinoire en plein air. **Malheureusement, / En fait,** il faisait très froid.

c Je voudrais aller au spectacle *Forêt enchantée*. **D'un autre côté, / En plus,** ça commence à 22 heures, c'est tard!

d Samedi, je vais en ville avec mes copines. **Par contre, / D'ailleurs,** ça tombe bien, j'ai besoin d'un nouveau jean.

e Le nouveau cinéma est très moderne. **En fait, / En revanche,** je trouve que les sièges ne sont pas confortables.

f J'ai visité une expo photos. Mes parents ont adoré. **En plus, / Franchement,** moi, j'ai trouvé ça très ennuyeux.

3 On paper, add another sentence to each sentence below, giving a clear opinion either positive or negative. Use an appropriate connective each time.

a Ma copine Lucie est très généreuse.

b Je m'entends bien avec Paul.

c Je n'aime pas la nouvelle pizzéria.

d Ma sortie préférée le samedi soir, c'est ...

3 How do I only use language that I know to be correct?

To get the highest grade in the exam, use impressive French, but don't overreach yourself. Only use complex language if you are sure it is correct.

1 You can combine the **imperfect** with the **perfect** tense to set the scene for an action. Complete the sentences using the correct tense of the verb given.

Example: Quand j'avais douze ans, je me suis cassé la jambe. (When I was 12, I broke my leg.)

a Nous [marcher] .... au bord de la mer quand nous [voir] .... un sous-marin jaune.

b Hier, il [rester] .... au lit parce qu'il [être] .... malade.

2 You can use the **imperfect** tense to talk about how things used to be. Complete the sentence to write **two** things about your childhood.

Example: *Quand j'étais petit, je rêvais d'être astronaute.*

Quand j'étais petit(e), ...

et ....

3 Reuse French sentence patterns you have seen in your lessons. For example, each English *-ing* form in the table translates differently into French according to the **context**. Now complete the two steps below for a–e.

Learn language in chunks, as part of a phrase or even a sentence, to familiarise yourself with French sentence patterns.

A Likes and dislikes	We enjoy cooking.	*Nous aimons faire la cuisine.*
B Descriptions	He's sitting on the bed.	*Il est assis sur le lit.*
C Leisure activities	They go skating after school.	*Elles font du skate après l'école.*
D Ongoing action in present	We are walking in the park.	*On se promène au parc.*
E Ongoing action in past	He was eating when we arrived.	*Il mangeait quand on est arrivés.*

i Label the following sentences **A–E** according to the context they belong to.

ii Then use the examples in the grid to help you translate them into French.

a ☐ He goes swimming on Mondays. ....

b ☐ My grandparents love reading. ....

c ☐ He was running when he fell over. ....

d ☐ She's wearing a blue jumper. ....

e ☐ They're doing their homework. ....

4 Take evasive action! If you are unsure about how to use the subjunctive, replace it with something simpler. Look at the example, then, on paper, write two French sentences to match a and b.

Example: 'Mum wants me to do sport' requires the subjunctive: *Maman veut que je* ***fasse*** *du sport.* Instead, you can write 'Mum says I must do sport' – *Maman dit que je dois* ***faire*** *du sport.*

a I would like my friend to be kinder. → I think my friend must be kinder.

b My friend wants us to go on holiday together. → My friend says we must go on holiday together.

Sample response

Now look at this exam-style writing task, similar to the one you saw on page 1.

Exam-style question

Les sorties en ville

Un forum francophone pose une question sur les sorties en ville.

Écris un message pour le forum. Tu **dois** faire référence aux points suivants:

- ce qu'on peut faire le soir dans ta ville
- les aspects positifs et négatifs de ces sorties
- ta dernière sortie
- ce que tu vas faire ce week-end.

Écris 80–90 mots environ **en français**. **(20 marks)**

Il y a des choses intéressantes à faire dans ma ville. Par exemple, je vais souvent au café Chez Fred avec mes amis, parce qu'on peut y jouer au baby-foot. En plus, je trouve que les boissons ne sont pas chères. Samedi dernier, c'était mon anniversaire et j'ai vu un film au cinéma du centre commercial. Malheureusement, c'est loin et il faut prendre le bus. Ce week-end, je vais aller à un concert de rock. Mon père dit que je ne dois pas sortir tard le soir, mais d'un autre côté, je pense que c'est une soirée exceptionnelle!

Leah

1 Has Leah addressed all the bullet points in the question? Note one example from her answer that addresses each point.

ce qu'on peut faire le soir	
les aspects positifs	
les aspects négatifs	
ta dernière sortie	
ce que tu vas faire ce week-end	

2 Which connectives does Leah use to express her opinions clearly? Note down four examples.

....

....

3 Leah uses good French sentence patterns. Find and note down one example of each of the following.

a combining the imperfect tense with the perfect tense ....

....

b saying 'you have to' ....

c saying 'I'm going to' ....

d saying 'My father doesn't want me to go out late at night' (without using the subjunctive)

....

Your turn!

You are now going to plan and write your own response to the exam-style question from page 1.

1. First jot down your ideas in French.

   Who will you write about? Two people are enough. ....

   What are their qualities? ....

   What was your friend like and what did you do together? Use both imperfect and perfect tenses.

   ....

   The fourth bullet invites you to talk about the future. One sentence can be enough.

   ....

2. Write your answer to the exam-style question. Then check your work using the checklist.

Checklist In my answer do I ...	✓
answer all the bullet points?	
give only relevant information?	
express clear opinions?	
use connectives (such as *en particulier* or *par contre*)?	
talk about the past, using the imperfect and the perfect tenses?	
combine the imperfect and perfect tenses in one sentence?	
talk about the future, using *aller* + infinitive?	
use accurate verb forms?	
use phrases that I know to be correct because I recognise the context they come from?	
use phrases that I know to be correct because I learned them as a chunk?	

Review your skills

Check up

Review your response to the exam-style question on page 7. Tick the column to show how well you think you have done each of the following.

	Not quite	Nearly there	Got it!
clearly addressed all the bullet points			
expressed opinions clearly			
only used language that I know to be correct			

Need more practice?

On paper, plan and write your response to the exam-style question below.

Exam-style question

Une personne que tu admires

Un forum francophone pose la question «Quelle personne admires-tu le plus?»

Écris un message pour le forum. Tu **dois** faire référence aux points suivants:

- la personne que tu admires
- les qualités de cette personne
- les actions les plus intéressantes de cette personne
- l'influence de cette personne sur tes projets d'avenir.

Écris 80–90 mots environ **en français**. **(20 marks)**

To write a good answer, try to include:

- a variety of structures
- examples of complex structures
- accurate language and structures to talk about past, present and future events
- creative language use, for example to express thoughts, ideas and feelings
- language used to interest and to convince the reader.

How confident do you feel about each of these **skills**? Colour in the bars.

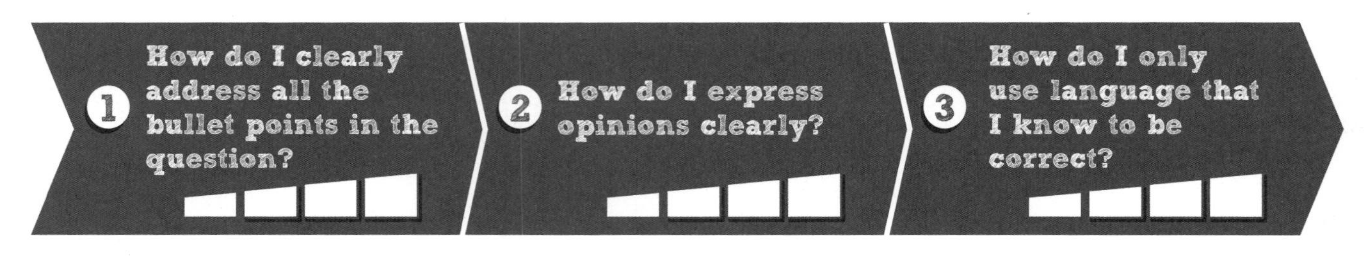

Get started

Giving a detailed answer

This unit will help you learn how to make your writing interesting and show off your French by making sure your text gives **all** the information required in appropriate detail. The skills you will build are to:

- make the most of adjectives
- make the most of adverbs
- expand on key points.

In the exam, you will be asked to tackle writing tasks such as the one below. This unit will prepare you to plan and write your own response to this question.

Exam-style question

Le cinéma

Ton ami(e) français(e) te demande ce que tu penses du cinéma sur un réseau social.

Écris une réponse à ton ami(e). Tu **dois** faire référence aux points suivants:

- où et quand tu as vu un film la dernière fois
- ton genre de film préféré
- les côtés positifs et négatifs de voir un film au cinéma
- ta prochaine sortie au cinéma.

Écris 80–90 mots environ **en français**. **(20 marks)**

The three key questions in the **skills boosts** will help you to add more detail to your writing.

How do I make the most of adjectives?

How do I make the most of adverbs?

How do I expand on key points?

Look at the sample student answer on the next page.

Read one student's answer to the exam-style question on page 9.

Exam-style question

Le cinéma

Ton ami(e) français(e) te demande ce que tu penses du cinéma sur un réseau social.

Écris une réponse à ton ami(e). Tu **dois** faire référence aux points suivants:

- où et quand tu as vu un film la dernière fois
- ton genre de film préféré
- les côtés positifs et négatifs de voir un film au cinéma
- ta prochaine sortie au cinéma.

Écris 80–90 mots environ **en français**. **(20 marks)**

Le week-end dernier, j'ai vu Blade Runner. C'est un film assez novateur, très atmosphérique et vraiment passionnant!

Pour moi, le genre de films le plus intéressant, c'est la science-fiction: généralement, il y a des effets spéciaux et souvent de bons acteurs, comme Harrison Ford.

Les avantages du cinéma sont, par exemple, le grand écran et les sièges confortables, mais Netflix est une façon plus pratique et moins chère de voir des films.

Le week-end prochain, j'irai au cinéma avec mes amis pour voir le dernier James Bond. J'ai hâte d'y être!

1. Has this student addressed all the bullet points? Answer these questions about his answer to check.
   - a. What is the last film he saw? ....
   - b. What is his favourite film genre? ....
   - c. What positive and negative aspects of going to the cinema does he mention? ....
   - d. What does he say about his next outing to the cinema? ....

2. Read the student's answer again. Complete the following activities.

   Some adjectives can go before AND after the noun, but their meaning usually changes: *dernier*: latest/last; *ancien*: previous/old

   - a. In French, list **three** adjectives used before the noun. ....
   - b. Circle **ten** adjectives used after the noun.
   - c. In French, list **three** adverbs of intensity (how much). ....
   - d. Underline **two** adverbs of frequency (how often).
   - e. Find and write down:

     one superlative expression ....

     two comparative expressions ....
   - f. Highlight **two** ways of introducing an example.

How do I make the most of adjectives?

Add interesting adjectives to make your writing more detailed and engaging. Remember: adjectives agree with the noun; they generally go after the noun but some come before; they can be used with a comparative or a superlative.

1. Replace each adjective which has been crossed out with a more interesting one from the box and write it above the crossed-out word. Make sure you pick one that has the correct agreement!

ennuyeux	excellents	
fatigantes	originales	
parfait	relaxante	passionnant

a Faire de la musique, c'est une activité très ~~cool~~.

b Je lis un livre ~~intéressant~~ mais certains passages sont assez ~~longs~~.

c La danse, c'est un sport ~~génial~~ pour la santé mais certaines leçons sont ~~difficiles~~!

d J'adore les séries françaises parce que les histoires sont ~~super~~ et les acteurs sont ~~bons~~!

2. Use both the adjectives in brackets to describe each underlined noun in these sentences. Add insertion marks in the correct positions and write the adjectives above. Remember to make them agree!

a *grosse* *noire*
J'ai une ^ chienne ^. Le dimanche, je mets un survêtement et je la sors à la campagne.
(gros /noir) (vieux / confortable)

b J'adore cette bande dessinée pour ses personnages et ses illustrations.
(nombreux / amusant) (beau / original)

c Mon passe-temps préféré, c'est faire des gâteaux avec des décorations.
(bon / appétissant) (joli / coloré)

In front of an adjective, *des* becomes *de*:
des livres → ***de** beaux livres*

3. Look at this student's notes and, on paper, write the sentences in full, using a comparative and a superlative.

+ lecture / les romans fantastiques ++ (intéressant) les romans policiers / +++ Lord of the Rings

Comparative:
plus (adjective) ***que***
moins (adjective) ***que***

Superlative:
le/la/les plus (adjective)
le/la/les moins (adjective)

Example: J'aime la lecture. **Pour moi,** les romans fantastiques **sont plus intéressants que** les romans policiers. **Je pense que** le roman **le plus intéressant**, c'est Lord of the Rings.

a *+ sport / le football – (exigeant) le rugby / – – le golf*

b *+ la télé / les documentaires ++ (informatif) les jeux télévisés / +++ Blue Planet*

c *+ le cinéma / les films romantiques – (ennuyeux) les films de science-fiction – –: Love Actually*

How do I make the most of adverbs?

Add interest to your text by using adverbs and adverbial phrases: they provide additional information about when, how, where, how often or to what degree something is done.

Their position can be a bit tricky. Learn a few rules.

1 **a** Write the adverbs listed below in the correct column in the grid.

bien	hier	toujours	récemment	gentiment	souvent
mal	assez	vraiment	beaucoup	rarement	demain

b Think of two more adverbs to add to each column.

When	How	How often	To what degree
maintenant	*probablement*	*parfois*	*tellement*

2 Cross out ~~cat~~ the adverb which is not positioned correctly in each sentence.

a Je **vraiment** suis **vraiment** passionnée de lecture.

b Je **toujours** télécharge **toujours** des livres sur ma liseuse.

c Je **rarement** lis **rarement** des bandes dessinées.

d Ma mère est **tellement** contente **tellement** quand je lis!

e Mon père pense que je ne suis pas **assez** active **assez**.

f Je ne fais **probablement** pas **probablement** assez de sport.

g Je **parfois** vais **parfois** à la piscine mais pas **souvent** assez **souvent**.

h Je **souvent** lis **souvent** le soir avant de dormir.

Adverbs which **modify a verb** usually <u>follow</u> the conjugated verb:

- *Je lis <u>beaucoup</u>.*
- *J'ai <u>beaucoup</u> lu.*
- *Je vais <u>beaucoup</u> lire.*

Adverbs which **modify an adjective or an adverb** are usually placed <u>*before*</u> it:

- *Je suis <u>très</u> active.*
- *Je suis <u>vraiment</u> très active.*

Adverbs of time often come <u>*at the start*</u> (or end) of the sentence:

- *<u>Aujourd'hui</u>, je lis un roman.*

3 On paper, rewrite this student's answer, replacing the asterisks with nine different adverbs from the grid in **1**.

Example: Je vais <u>assez</u> <u>souvent</u> au cinéma …

*Je vais * * au cinéma de l'Institut français parce que les films français m'intéressent *.*

** , j'ai vu un film avec Gad Elmaleh, un acteur que j'aime *. Je trouve qu'il joue * * bien!*

*Ma sœur, qui n'aime pas le cinéma, est * venue avec moi, alors *, en échange, je vais aller au match de foot avec elle!*

3 How do I expand on key points?

Another good way to expand on a key point is to follow it up with a specific fact that is relevant to the question. You can do this by:

- adding an example, an explanation or a contradictory statement, introduced by an appropriate connective
- saying what you did (past tense) or will do (future tense) using an adverb of time.

1 Fill in the gaps in these answers to the question *Quel est ton genre de film préféré?* using one of these connectives.

comme *(like)*	surtout *(especially)*	en effet *(indeed)*
par exemple *(for example)*	mais *(but)*	sauf *(except)*
par contre *(on the other hand)*		

You can use *comme* and *par exemple* separately or together.
The same applies to *mais* and *par contre*.

a J'aime bien les films de guerre, ... je trouve certains un peu trop violents.

b J'aime particulièrement les films de science-fiction, ... *Avatar* parce que je l'ai trouvé très ennuyeux.

c J'adore les films d'espionnage, ... les films de James Bond, parce qu'à mon avis, ce sont les plus amusants!

d Je suis passionné de films historiques, ... *Vikings* que j'ai trouvé passionnant.

2 Draw lines to match up the sentence halves in a way that makes sense and fits the topic: *Tes préférences pour les loisirs en famille.*

Pay attention to the time phrases as they determine the tense which follows.

A En général, j'aime bien faire du sport avec mes sœurs. Demain, ...	**a** nous avons fait 45 kilomètres. C'était assez fatigant mais très sympa!
B Tous les week-ends, ma famille et moi allons au cinéma. La semaine dernière, ...	**b** on regardera tous ensemble les émissions sportives.
C De temps en temps, je fais du vélo avec mon père. Hier, ...	**c** nous jouerons ensemble au tennis, ça sera génial.
D J'adore regarder la télévision en famille. Le week-end prochain, ...	**d** nous avons vu un film français vraiment très amusant.

3 Complete these sentences on the topic of *Tes préférences en musique.* Use connectives and present, past and future tenses as appropriate.

Example: J'adore la musique classique, sauf *la musique de Bach car je trouve ça ennuyeux.*

a Je vais souvent à des concerts; en effet, ...

b Le week-end dernier, je ....

c J'écoute souvent la radio, surtout ....

d Comme je joue bien du violon, l'année prochaine, je ....

e J'aime bien jouer du violon mais par contre, ...

Sample response

Now look at this exam-style writing task, similar to the one you saw on page 9.
Read the two student answers below.

Exam-style question

Les sorties en ville

Un(e) ami(e) te pose des questions sur tes sorties préférées. Réponds-lui dans un mail.

Tu **dois** faire référence aux points suivants:

- avec qui tu sors normalement
- ce que tu fais en ville
- une sortie récente
- tes projets de sortie pour le week-end prochain.

Écris 80–90 environ mots **en français**. **(20 marks)**

A

Normalement, je sors avec ma copine Sophie: elle est intéressante, amusante et excentrique! Nous allons généralement au centre commercial. Là, il y a beaucoup de magasins, par exemple Décathlon. J'aime beaucoup faire du shopping.

Le week-end dernier, je suis allé au cinéma avec mes parents. Nous avons vu un film de science-fiction. Ce n'était pas super. Le week-end prochain, je ferai une partie de tennis avec mon copain Max. C'est un grand sportif et il aime bien jouer au tennis avec moi. Après, nous irons manger une pizza en ville.

B

Je sors le plus souvent avec ma meilleure copine Léa parce qu'on s'entend très bien mais j'aime aussi beaucoup sortir avec ma famille. En ville, Léa et moi allons régulièrement dans des salons de thé. Par exemple, hier, nous sommes allées à Starbuck qui, selon moi, est le café le plus accueillant!

Le week-end dernier, j'ai visité le zoo avec ma famille. Comme nous nous sommes vraiment bien amusés, c'était une journée absolument inoubliable! Le week-end prochain, je finirai d'abord mes devoirs et ensuite, j'irai probablement au cinéma avec Léa.

① Complete the table to help you compare the two students' answers.

Which answer ...	A	B	How is this done? (explain or note examples from the text)
answers the question fully?	✓	✓	*by addressing all four bullet points*
gives relevant facts only?			
uses interesting adjectives?			
uses correct adjective agreement?			
positions adjectives correctly?			
uses a comparative or a superlative?			
uses adverbs appropriately?			
expands on key points?			
uses connectives to explain/illustrate?			
uses past and/or future tenses?			

② On paper, write your own answer to the exam-style question above. Use the table to help you.

When using three adjectives together, remember to add *et* before the last one:
C'est un passe-temps créatif, amusant ***et*** *passionnant!*

Your turn!

You are now going to plan and write your response to the exam-style question from page 9.

1. First jot down your ideas, concentrating on relevant details for each bullet point. Make sure you can say what you want to say in French!

   Where and when you last saw a film:

   Your favourite type of film:

   Positive and negative aspects of seeing a film in a cinema:

   Your next trip to the cinema:

2. Write your answer to the exam-style question. Then check your work using the checklist.

Checklist In my answer do I ...	✓
address all the bullet points?	
give lots of information?	
give only relevant information?	
use interesting adjectives?	
position adjectives correctly and use the correct agreement?	
use adverbs in the correct positions?	
use comparatives and/or superlatives?	
expand on key points?	
use appropriate connectives to illustrate or explain?	
say what I did/what I will do?	

Review your skills

Check up

Review your response to the exam-style question on page 15. Tick the column to show how well you think you have done each of the following.

	Not quite	Nearly there	Got it!
made the most of adjectives	☐	☐	☐
made the most of adverbs	☐	☐	☐
expanded on key points	☐	☐	☐

Need more practice?

On paper, plan and write your response to the exam-style question below.

Exam-style question

Les réseaux sociaux

Un magazine français pose des questions à ses lecteurs au sujet des réseaux sociaux.

Écris une réponse au magazine. Tu **dois** faire référence aux points suivants:

- ton réseau social préféré
- les avantages et les inconvénients des réseaux sociaux
- ta dernière communication sur un réseau social
- ce que tu feras en ligne ce soir.

Écris 80–90 mots environ **en français**. (20 marks)

To write a good answer in the short writing task you need to:

- address all the bullet points with relevant points
- expand on main points and ideas
- give your opinions convincingly
- use three time frames, e.g. present, past and future
- use varied and interesting vocabulary
- use complex and extended sentences.

How confident do you feel about each of these **skills**? Colour in the bars.

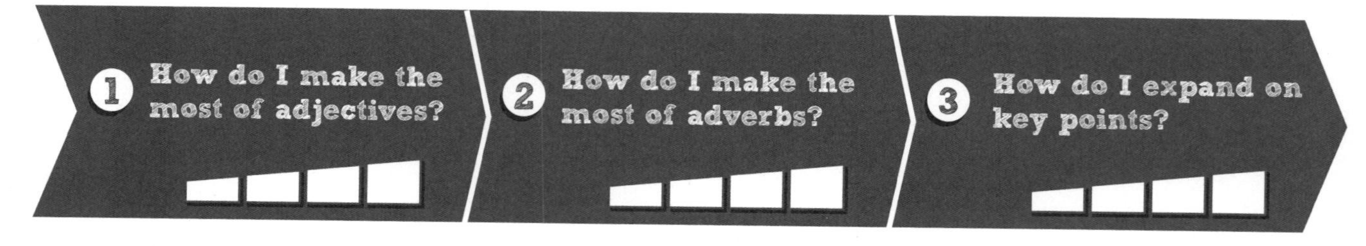

Get started

3 Using a wide range of vocabulary

This unit will help you use a wide range of vocabulary. The skills you will build are to:

- use a wider variety of verbs
- use a wider variety of adjectives
- learn French idioms and use them in the right way.

In the exam, you will be asked to tackle a writing task such as the one below. This unit will prepare you to plan and write your own response to this question, using a wide range of vocabulary.

Exam-style question

Article

Un magazine français cherche des articles sur les habitudes alimentaires des jeunes.

Écrivez un article sur vos repas pour intéresser les lecteurs.

Vous **devez** faire référence aux points suivants:

- où et quand vous mangez habituellement
- ce qui est important pour vous dans les repas
- un repas mémorable
- vos repas quand vous serez adulte.

Justifiez vos idées et vos opinions.
Écrivez 130–150 mots environ **en français**. **(28 marks)**

The three key questions in the **skills boosts** will help you to use a wide range of vocabulary.

How do I use a wider variety of verbs?

How do I use a wider variety of adjectives?

How do I use idioms?

Look at the sample student answer on the next page.

Read one student's answer to the exam-style question on page 17.

> *Je suis convaincu que faire des repas réguliers, c'est important pour garder la forme. Les jours d'école, je prends un petit déjeuner copieux. C'est essentiel pour bien démarrer la journée et ça vaut la peine de se lever plus tôt. Le week-end, je me lève tard et mes parents préparent un brunch. On bavarde, c'est un moment convivial et détendu. Quand j'étais petit, le goûter était mon repas préféré et je dévorais des gâteaux après l'école. Maintenant, je mange plus équilibré mais j'apprécie toujours un fruit à quatre heures.*
>
> *J'ai fait un repas de Noël inoubliable chez mes grands-parents. Tous les plats étaient savoureux. J'ai mangé comme quatre mais j'avais les yeux plus grands que le ventre et je n'ai pas fini mon dessert. Ensuite, nous avons joué à des jeux de société. Quand j'aurai des enfants, j'espère que nous continuerons cette tradition mais aussi que nous partagerons tous les jours un repas en famille.*
>
> *James*

1. James mentions four types of meals. Find and circle the French equivalent for:

   a breakfast **b** brunch **c** afternoon snack/tea **d** Christmas lunch

2. James uses varied vocabulary in his answer. First, look at the adjectives. Note down how James says each of the following, instead of using the obvious choices given in brackets.

   a a **large** breakfast (*un* ***gros*** *petit déjeuner*) ....
   b it's **important** (*c'est* ***important***) ....
   c a **pleasant** time (shared with others) (*un moment* ***sympa***) ....
   d **memorable** (***mémorable***) ....
   e **delicious** (***délicieux***) ....

3. With verbs too, James tries to go beyond the obvious choices.

   i **Without looking at the text**, translate these phrases into French as best you can.
   ii Then look at the text and note down what James actually wrote.

   a I really think that ....
   b to start the day ....
   c to chat ....
   d I used to eat a lot of ....
   e I enjoy ....

4. In the exam, you are expected to make references to the past (using the perfect and/or imperfect tenses) and the future. Write the main tense(s) you will need for each bullet point.

   - où et quand vous mangez habituellement ....
   - ce qui est important pour vous dans les repas ....
   - un repas mémorable ....
   - vos repas quand vous serez adulte ....

How do I use a wider variety of verbs?

- Collect synonyms for common verbs.
- Note them in phrases, as some are more suitable than others in a given context.

① In your writing, try to extend your options beyond the most obvious verbs. Complete this spidergram using an alternative to *aimer* in each sentence.

ça m'amuse (used for something funny)
ça me plaît (= general liking)
j'adore (= strong liking)
j'aime bien (often used for moderate liking)
j'apprécie (often used when comparing two likes)
je me régale avec (used for particularly delicious food)

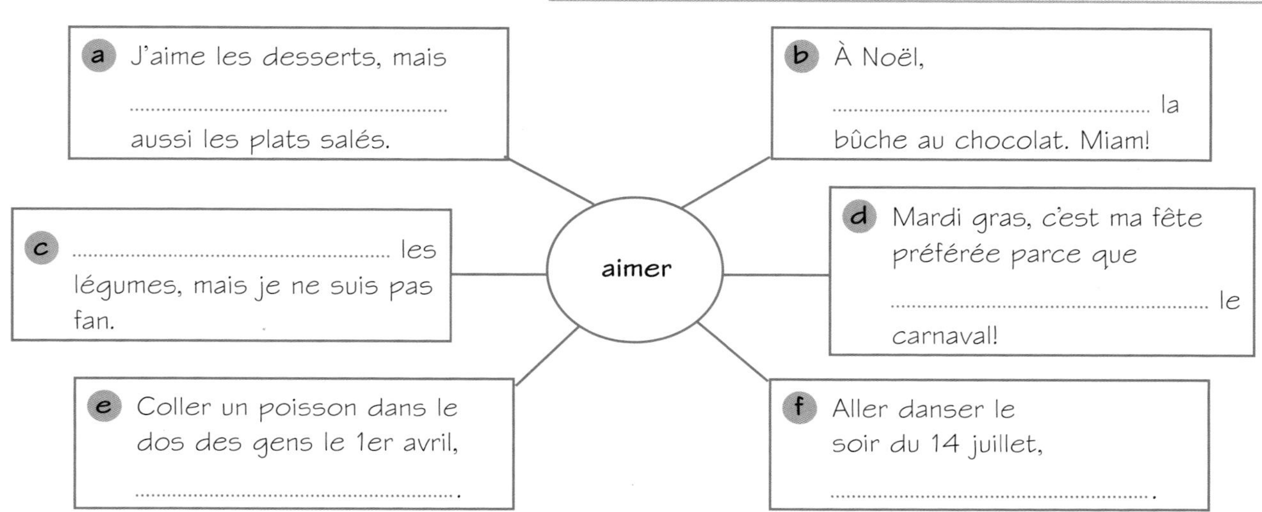

② In this example, the verb *dire*, 'to say', could be replaced with another, more precise verb.

Le guide ***dit*** *que le carnaval n'est pas une tradition ancienne.* – The guide says the Carnival isn't an old tradition.

Draw lines to match these alternatives to *dire* with their meanings.

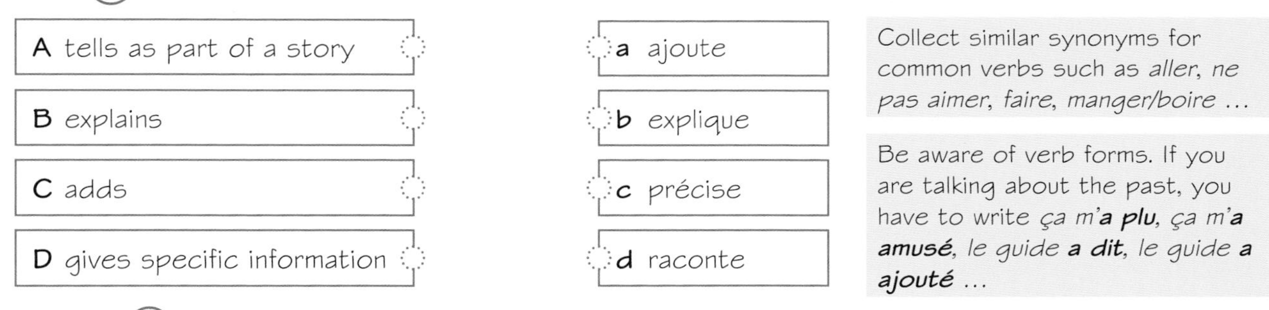

Collect similar synonyms for common verbs such as *aller*, *ne pas aimer*, *faire*, *manger/boire* …

Be aware of verb forms. If you are talking about the past, you have to write *ça m'****a plu****, ça m'****a amusé****, le guide* ***a dit****, le guide* ***a ajouté*** …

③ Replace the underlined phrases by writing a suitable synonym above each one.

Mon copain voudrait aller au carnaval parce qu'il aime les chars fleuris. Moi aussi, j'aime les chars, mais je ne suis pas fan. J'ai dit qu'il y a trop de monde au carnaval et j'ai aussi dit que tout est cher dans les cafés. Il a dit qu'il ne veut pas aller au carnaval le samedi mais le vendredi, parce qu'il y a moins de monde. J'ai accepté, parce que même si je ne suis pas fan des chars, j'aime la musique. En plus, les sucreries, j'aime ça et je vais aimer les gaufres au Nutella!

2 How do I use a wider variety of adjectives?

- Collect synonyms or near-synonyms for common adjectives, especially those that can be used to express and justify opinions such as *beau, bon, mauvais* ...
- Note the synonyms as part of a phrase, as they could have a slightly different meaning.

1 a Read the student's response below and cross out ~~cat~~ all the bland or ordinary adjectives and qualifiers. One has been done for you. There are 10 more to find.

b Replace the adjectives with more interesting ones from the box by writing them above. (Remember to make them agree with the nouns.)

Most adjectives go after the noun: *une fête conviviale.* Some short and common adjectives go before: *une belle fête.* In the plural, the indefinite article changes according to the position: ***des*** *fêtes conviviales*, but ***de*** *belles fêtes.*

Quand mon père et sa compagne Cécile se sont mariés, ils ont organisé une ~~belle~~ fête ^ (conviviale). Pour commencer, un vendeur de glaces est venu sur son tricycle! C'était bien et les glaces étaient bonnes. Il y avait un très bon orchestre de jazz. On a aussi organisé un lâcher de ballons. C'était beau et Cécile a un peu pleuré. Pendant le dîner, le père de Cécile a raconté de mauvaises blagues, mais tout le monde souriait. La seule chose négative, c'était le temps, parce qu'il a plu toute la journée. En plus, les enfants couraient partout, c'était nul. Après le dîner, on a servi un très gros et très beau gâteau. Au final, c'était une très bonne fête. Quels bons souvenirs!

agaçant (*annoying/irritating*)
convivial (*convivial – often implying the sharing of food*)
décevant (*disappointing*)
délicieux (*delicious*)
divertissant (*entertaining*)
émouvant (*moving*)
inoubliable (*unforgettable*)
original (*interesting and unexpected*)
réussi (*successful*)
ridicule (*ridiculous*)
superbe (*impressive, on a large scale*)

2 Write three sentences about aspects of these family celebrations. Add at least three different interesting adjectives each time.

a l'anniversaire de mon grand-père: le gâteau, l'ambiance

....

....

b le réveillon de Noël: le repas, les chants traditionnels

....

....

c le mariage de ma cousine: la robe de la mariée, la musique

....

....

3 How do I use idioms?

Idioms are expressions that are specific to a language and cannot be translated word for word. For example, two French idioms are *chez moi* (at my house) and *chez nous* (in our house/area/country). A well-chosen idiom will make your writing more authentic and convincing, but learn them in context to make sure you know exactly what they mean.

1. Look at these sentences (some are extracts from James's text on page 18). They each contain an idiom. Write the letter of the English equivalent in each box. Then highlight the idiom in each French sentence.

   a Faire des repas réguliers, c'est important pour garder la forme. ☐
   b Ça vaut la peine de se lever plus tôt. ☐
   c Tous les plats étaient savoureux et j'ai mangé comme quatre. ☐
   d J'avais les yeux plus gros que le ventre et je n'ai pas fini mon dessert. ☐
   e Quand je vais à l'étranger, la cuisine française, ça me manque. ☐
   f Souvent, je donne un coup de main aux organisateurs du festival. ☐
   g La fête de la musique, ça me tient à cœur parce que je suis musicien. ☐

A my eyes were bigger than my belly	B I miss it	C it is worth it	D to keep fit
E it is close to my heart	F I give a helping hand	G I ate like a horse	

2. Complete these sentences with an appropriate idiom from 1.

   It's a good idea to place one or two idioms in your written French.

   a .... d'aller au carnaval de la Guadeloupe, même si c'est loin.
   b Quand mes parents sont absents, les repas en famille, ...
   c Aller au mariage de mon frère, ... parce que je vais être témoin.
   d Le samedi, ... à mon père pour faire le ménage.

   In your own writing in French, adjust the pronoun and the verb form if necessary:
   *Ma grand-mère ne danse plus, mais ça **lui** manque.*
   *Après l'entraînement à la piscine, je **mange** comme quatre.*

3. Look again at sentences a, e and g in 1. What difference do you notice between each sentence and its English equivalent below? Complete the statement below.

   a Having regular meals is important to stay fit.
   e When I go abroad, I miss French cooking.
   g The Music Festival is close to my heart because I'm a musician.

   In the French sentences, there is an extra .... and an extra word (.................... or ....).

   This structure is very common in French and an easy way of sounding more idiomatic.

4. On paper, write a more idiomatic version of each French translation.

   a My favourite ice cream is lemon sorbet. – Ma glace préférée est le sorbet au citron.
   b I really enjoyed the concert. – Le concert m'a beaucoup plu.
   c I try to eat healthily, but I miss chocolate. – J'essaie de manger équilibré, mais le chocolat me manque.

Sample response

Now look at this exam-style writing task, similar to the one you saw on page 17.

Exam-style question

Venez à notre festival!

Votre ville est jumelée avec une ville en France.

Écrivez une lettre pour convaincre le comité de jumelage de venir à un festival dans votre région.

Vous **devez** faire référence aux points suivants:

- ce que vous pensez des festivals en général
- ce que vous aimez dans ce festival
- comment vous avez participé au festival
- comment le festival va se développer à l'avenir.

Madame, Monsieur,

Je suis convaincue que les festivals sont une expérience non seulement distrayante, mais aussi enrichissante. Dans notre ville, FolkFest, c'est un festival de danse folk. Les spectacles sont variés et divertissants. Les visiteurs apprécient aussi la musique, qui est souvent entraînante, mais aussi touchante et pleine d'émotion. FolkFest, c'est un festival qui me tient à cœur parce que j'y participe depuis longtemps. Quand j'avais 8 ans, je suis montée sur scène avec ma classe. Cette soirée, c'était une expérience inoubliable. L'année dernière, j'ai donné un coup de main au comité d'organisation. Par exemple, j'ai renseigné les visiteurs et j'ai aidé les spectateurs qui s'étaient perdus.

Les organisateurs ont annoncé que l'année prochaine, il y aura plus de spectacles interactifs, avec participation des spectateurs. J'espère donc que nous accueillerons beaucoup de visiteurs de votre ville, car ça vaut la peine de faire le voyage.

Cordialement, Leila

1 Note down the more creative verb that Leila uses instead of the underlined verb in each phrase below.

a. je pense que ....

b. les visiteurs aiment aussi la musique ....

c. j'ai parlé avec les visiteurs ....

d. j'espère donc qu'il y aura beaucoup de visiteurs ....

2 Note down the adjectives with the following meanings that Leila uses.

entertaining .... / ....

life-enhancing .... varied ....

lively .... touching ....

moving .... unforgettable ....

When you collect vocabulary, note phrases with a noun + adjective, e.g. *une expérience distrayante*, and reuse them where you can in your writing.

3 How does Leila emphasise the following statements? Highlight the equivalent French statements in the text.

a. FolkFest is a folk dance festival.

b. FolkFest is a festival that's close to my heart.

c. That evening was an unforgettable experience.

Your turn!

You are now going to plan and write your response to the exam-style question from page 17.

Exam-style question

Article

Un magazine français cherche des articles sur les habitudes alimentaires des jeunes.

Écrivez un article sur vos repas pour intéresser les lecteurs.

Vous **devez** faire référence aux points suivants:

- où et quand vous mangez habituellement
- ce qui est important pour vous dans les repas
- un repas mémorable
- vos repas quand vous serez adulte.

Justifiez vos idées et vos opinions. Écrivez 130–150 mots environ **en français.** **(28 marks)**

1. First jot down your ideas in French. Note interesting verbs, adjectives and idioms.

   Which daily meals could you talk about? ....

   ....

   Which meals matter to you, and why? What, when and where do you eat? Who with?

   ....

   Think of two or three memorable meals. Choose the one that you have most to say about.

   ....

2. Write your answer to the exam-style question. Then check your work using the checklist.

....

....

....

....

....

....

....

....

....

....

....

....

....

Checklist In my answer do I …	✓
answer both bullet points?	
give only relevant information?	
express clear opinions and justify them?	
try my best to convince the reader?	
use varied verbs, not just the most obvious ones?	
talk about the past **and** the future?	
use correct verb forms?	
use specific adjectives, especially to express opinions?	
apply correct adjective agreements?	

Review your skills

Check up

Review your response to the exam-style question on page 23. Tick the column to show how well you think you have done each of the following.

	Not quite	Nearly there	Got it!
used a wider variety of verbs			
used a wider variety of adjectives			
learned and used idiomatic expressions appropriately			

Need more practice?

On paper, plan and write your response to the exam-style question below.

Exam-style question

Une fête de famille

Un magazine français cherche des articles sur les fêtes de famille dans d'autres pays.

Écrivez un article sur une fête récente dans votre famille pour intéresser les lecteurs.

Vous **devez** faire référence aux points suivants:

- ce que vous pensez des fêtes de famille en général
- une fête de famille récente
- pourquoi vous avez aimé cette fête
- votre prochaine fête de famille.

Justifiez vos idées et vos opinions. Écrivez 130–150 mots environ **en français**. (28 marks)

To write a good answer, try to include:

- varied vocabulary, with many examples of uncommon language
- creative language use, for example to express thoughts, ideas and feelings
- language used to interest the reader
- appropriate style and register
- varied grammatical structures, including complex ones
- well-linked sentences
- references to past, present and future events.

How confident do you feel about each of these **skills**? Colour in the bars.

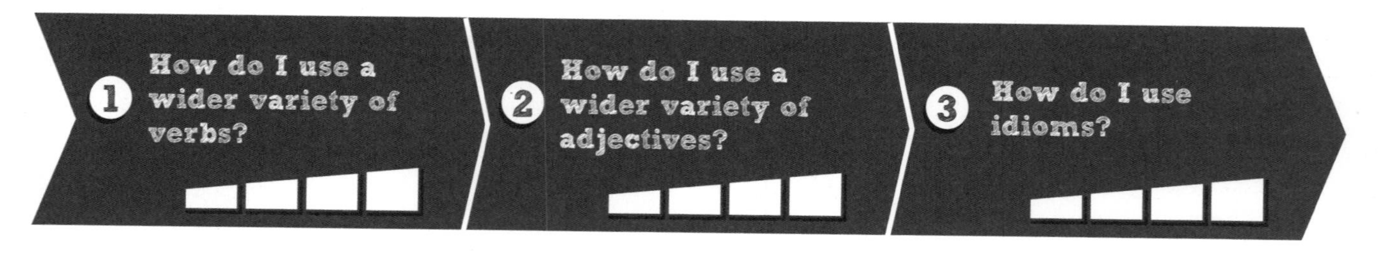

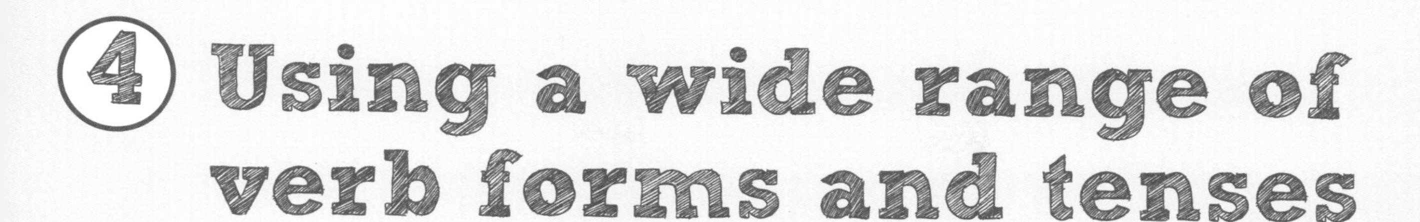

4 Using a wide range of verb forms and tenses

This unit will help you learn how to vary verb forms and verb tenses to show off your knowledge of grammar. The skills you will build are to:

- use different persons of the verb
- use a variety of past tenses
- use different ways of writing about the future.

In the exam, you will be asked to tackle writing tasks such as the one below. This unit will prepare you to plan and write your own response to this question.

Exam-style question

Ma ville

Un magazine français pour les jeunes fait une enquête: «Votre ville est-elle la ville idéale?»

Écrivez une lettre à la rédaction du magazine pour donner des informations sur votre ville.

Vous **devez** faire référence aux points suivants:

- votre ville et ce que vous y aimez
- en quoi votre ville s'est améliorée récemment
- les projets pour les jeunes dans votre ville
- ce que vous aimeriez avoir dans la ville.

Justifiez vos idées et vos opinions.
Écrivez 130–150 mots environ **en français**. (28 marks)

The three key questions in the **skills boosts** will help you to use a wide range of verb forms and tenses when writing in French.

1 How do I use different persons of the verb?

2 How do I use a variety of past tenses?

3 How do I use different ways of writing about the future?

Look at the sample student answer on the next page.

Read one student's answer to the exam-style question on page 25.

Je vis à Plouester, une petite ville en Bretagne. Ma famille et moi habitons ici depuis douze ans et on adore la ville. En effet, elle est agréable, située au bord de la mer et elle a un microclimat: l'idéal pour les gens qui, comme moi, aiment la plage.

Quand j'étais petit, il n'y avait rien à faire l'hiver pour les jeunes et c'était assez déprimant. Depuis l'année dernière, c'est beaucoup mieux. Comme beaucoup de familles avaient contacté le maire et lui avaient dit que les enfants s'ennuyaient, la commune a construit un nouveau centre sportif.*

Le maire a aussi l'intention d'ouvrir une maison des jeunes l'année prochaine. Quand elle ouvrira, on pourra y faire du théâtre et des activités artistiques. On va bien s'amuser!

Si possible, j'aimerais avoir un cinéma multi-salles au centre-ville. Si le maire était d'accord, Plouester serait un paradis!

* le maire – *the mayor*

1 Read Yann's answer above. Find and note down:

a three reasons why Yann finds Plouester an ideal place to live

....

b one recent change that has improved the town, and the reason for this change

....

c one future change that will improve the town further for young people

....

d something that Yann thinks would make his town ideal

....

2 Yann has used a variety of tenses and persons of the verb. Note all the verb forms in the correct column.

Use the pluperfect to describe something that **had** taken place before something else happened:
***j'étais** parti(e)* – I had left
***j'avais** visité* – I had visited

Pluperfect	Imperfect	Perfect	Present	Near future/Future	Conditional

3 **a** In the first paragraph, Yann uses a variety of subjects to avoid saying *je* all the time. Find and highlight:

i a subject equivalent to *nous*

ii a subject equivalent to *ils/elles*

b In the third paragraph, Yann uses different ways of talking about the future. Underline them in the text.

How do I use different persons of the verb?

You have learned all the different forms of many verbs, regular and irregular, so don't let that knowledge go to waste – use it to impress! Use *je* of course, but also create opportunities to use other subject pronouns.

1. Rewrite each sentence using the subject and verb given in brackets to avoid using *je*.

Example: Samedi matin, j'ai joué au foot au stade avec mon équipe. (mon équipe – jouer)

Samedi matin, mon équipe et moi avons joué au foot au stade.

a. Samedi après-midi, je suis allé au cinéma avec des amis. (mes amis et moi – aller)

b. Je n'ai pas aimé le film, mes copains non plus. (personne – aimer)

c. Dimanche, je suis allée au restaurant avec mes parents. (mes parents – m'inviter)

d. J'ai eu un super cadeau de la part de ma sœur. (ma sœur – me donner)

e. J'ai beaucoup ri et je me suis bien amusé. (on – rire/s'amuser)

f. Voilà ce que j'ai fait ce week-end en ville. Et toi? (tu – faire)

g. En général, j'aime beaucoup aller en ville le week-end. (ça – me plaire de)

2. Rewrite this short text, avoiding using *je* whenever you can.

J'habite à Vannes avec ma mère et ma sœur. J'ai un assez petit appartement situé au centre-ville. Je trouve les gens accueillants ici. Comme tous les visiteurs, j'apprécie aussi la beauté de la ville. Je vais souvent à la plage avec ma sœur. Après, j'aime aller faire du shopping ensemble dans la zone piétonne.

How to avoid using *je*:

- Talk about several people, not just yourself: *nous, on*
- Say *et moi* rather than *je … avec*: *mon équipe et moi avons joué …*
- Talk about other people: *mes parents, ma sœur, etc.*
- Think of other people's viewpoint: *mon copain adore …*

2 How do I use a variety of past tenses?

When a question requires you to write about the past, create opportunities to use more than one past tense. Use the:

- perfect tense – to say what you did
- imperfect tense – to describe what it was like or what you used to do
- pluperfect tense – to say what had happened before something else took place.

1 Read Lucas's answers to a question about *Une visite mémorable.* Underline all the verbs in the pluperfect. Then draw lines to link the sentence halves.

When you write about what you did, you could also add what had happened before.

A Nous voulions aller à Marseille car	**a** le train était déjà parti.
B J'ai voulu prendre le train comme	**b** je ne l'avais jamais pris avant.
C Catastrophe! Quand nous sommes arrivés à la gare,	**c** ma mère avait acheté des billets à l'avance sur Internet.
D Nous avons longtemps cherché un hôtel car	**d** nous n'avions encore jamais visité cette ville.
E On est allés visiter le château d'If parce qu'	**e** nous n'avions pas réservé de chambres.
F On n'a pas fait la queue pour y entrer parce que	**f** on avait vu un documentaire sur cette île-prison. Ça semblait super!

2 Complete the sentences which Lucas has started about his memorable visit.

- Use one verb in the pluperfect to speak about something which had happened.
- Use one verb in the imperfect to give an opinion.

Example: Avant le dîner, nous avons bu un apéritif local qu'*on nous avait recommandé. Il était excellent!*

a Après l'apéritif, nous avons mangé un plat local que/qu' ....

....

b Le matin suivant, nous étions très fatigués parce que/qu' ....

....

c En plus ma mère pleurait parce que/qu' ....

....

3 On paper, translate these sentences into French.

a The train has just left, you are too late.

b I have just bought my train ticket.

c The train had just left when I arrived at the station.

d We had just finished our visit when the park closed.

Use *venir (juste/à peine) de* + infinitive to mean you have just done something. Adding *juste* or *à peine* is optional in French.

I have just come back – *je viens (juste/à peine) de rentrer*

I had just come back – *je venais (juste/à peine) de rentrer … quand tu es arrivé*

3 How do I use different ways of writing about the future?

Try to create opportunities to write about the future. You can do this by using:

- a time phrase which indicates the future: *demain, la semaine prochaine*
- a verb in the near future or future tense: *je vais sortir / on sortira ensemble*
- a verb in the conditional: *je sortirais (si je pouvais).*

1 Read this email written to an exchange partner who is coming to stay in the summer. Complete the grid.

> Quand tu viendras cet été à Bordeaux, on visitera la région. On va faire beaucoup de choses et tu vas bien t'amuser! Par exemple, je veux te montrer le centre-ville et, s'il fait beau, on ira aussi au bord de la mer. J'ai envie d'aller à la plage et j'aimerais faire du vélo dans la forêt avec toi.
>
> J'ai l'intention de te montrer la ville de Biarritz et j'espère qu'on aura le temps d'aller à la dune du Pilat. Si c'est possible, je voudrais y grimper!
>
> J'ai décidé de t'emmener chez mes grands-parents dans les Pyrénées. Je rêve de vivre dans les Pyrénées. Si je pouvais, j'habiterais dans une ferme! À bientôt!

a Words/phrases which indicate the future	**c** Verbs in the future tense
quand + future tense, je veux + infinitive	*tu viendras*
b Verbs in the near future	**d** Verbs in the conditional
on va faire	*j'aimerais + infinitive*

2 A student wants to write about what she will do with a friend who is visiting. Write the following sentences in French using structures from the grid in **1**.

a When my friend comes, we'll go to the market.

....

b If we have time, we'll visit the castle. ....

c If it was less far, we'd go to the beach. ....

d I hope that we will be able to go for a walk by the seaside.

....

e I dream of hiking in the countryside. ....

f I intend to show the old town to my friend. ....

g I have decided to go on a boat trip. ....

3 On paper, write six of your own sentences, each using a different structure.

Sample response

This is a writing task of the type you will have to do in the exam. Read Aidan's answer below.

Exam-style question

Ma région

Votre correspondant(e) français(e) vous pose des questions sur votre région préférée.

Écrivez un billet pour le site web de son collège avec des informations sur cette région.

Vous **devez** faire référence aux points suivants:

- ce que vous aimez dans cette région
- ce qui vous plaît moins
- un séjour récent dans cette région
- votre prochaine visite dans cette région.

Justifiez vos idées et vos opinions. Écrivez 130–150 mots environ **en français**. **(28 marks)**

J'adore le Yorkshire car les paysages sont spectaculaires, les gens accueillants et on y mange bien.

Ce que j'aime moins, c'est le temps: il est très imprévisible. En plus, c'est difficile de se déplacer si on n'a pas de voiture car il y a peu de bus.

Je viens de passer un week-end inoubliable à York avec ma famille. Nous étions dans un hôtel formidable que des amis avaient recommandé. On a visité le musée des Vikings: il y avait une longue queue mais ma mère avait réservé en ligne alors on n'a pas attendu. C'était génial! Il faisait beau et nous nous sommes promenés à la campagne. Superbe!

On va bientôt retourner dans le Yorkshire. Si je pouvais, j'irais là-bas tous les week-ends!

J'espère qu'un jour tu pourras y aller avec moi. J'aimerais te montrer cette région fantastique. Si tu viens, on fera une randonnée dans les Yorkshire Dales!

① Has Aidan followed the advice and used a wide range of verb forms and tenses? Complete the table with examples from the text.

subjects other than *je*	*les paysages*
verbs in the present tense	
verbs in the perfect tense	
verbs in the imperfect tense	
verbs in the pluperfect tense	
a phrase about the very recent past	
verbs in the near future	
verbs in the future tense	
verbs in the conditional	
phrases which indicate the future	

Your turn!

You are now going to plan and write your response to the exam-style question from page 25.

1. First jot down your ideas in French, concentrating on opportunities to vary the verb forms that you use.

   Briefly describe your town ....

   and its good points ....

   Recent improvements ....

   What made them happen? ....

   What improvement will take place? ....

   What will young people be able to do then? ....

   What else would you like in your town? ....

2. Write your answer to the question on page 25. Then check your work using the checklist.

Checklist In my answer do I ...	✓
use verbs in the present tense?	
use verbs in the perfect tense?	
use verbs in the imperfect tense?	
use verbs in the pluperfect tense?	
use verbs in the near future/future tense?	
use verbs in the conditional?	
use a variety of subjects/subject pronouns?	
use the correct verb endings?	
use phrases which indicate a future tense?	

Review your skills

Check up

Review your response to the exam-style question on page 31. Tick the column to show how well you think you have done each of the following.

	Not quite	Nearly there	Got it!
used different persons of the verb			
used a variety of past tenses			
used different ways of writing about the future			

Need more practice?

On paper, plan and write your response to the exam-style question below.

Exam-style question

Un projet communautaire

Le site web de votre ville jumelée* en France vous demande un article sur un projet communautaire de jeunes de votre ville.

Écrivez un article pour donner des informations sur ce projet pour intéresser les lecteurs.

Vous **devez** faire référence aux points suivants:

- pourquoi ce projet est nécessaire
- en quoi ce projet consiste
- une action pour réaliser ce projet
- votre participation à cette action.

Justifiez vos idées et vos opinions.

Écrivez 130–150 mots environ **en français**. **(28 marks)**

* jumelée = *twinned*

To write a good answer in the long writing task you need to:

- address all four bullet points
- give detailed information
- communicate and develop your ideas clearly
- narrate events, inform and keep the reader interested
- use uncommon vocabulary
- give and justify your opinions
- use linking words to write complex sentences
- use the appropriate style and register
- use verb forms and at least three tenses accurately.

How confident do you feel about each of these **skills**? Colour in the bars.

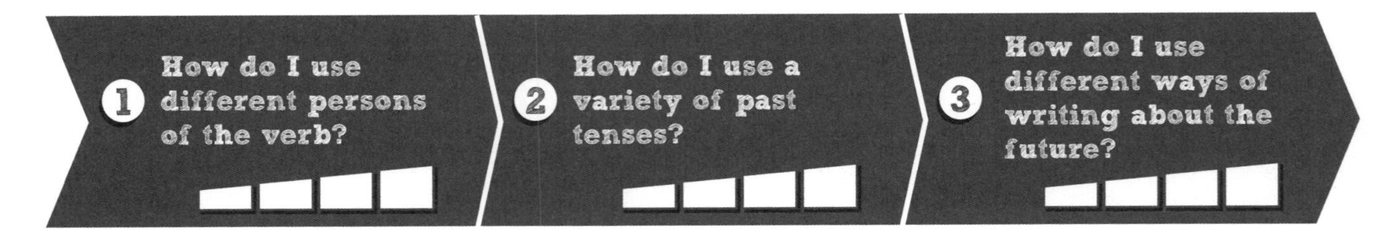

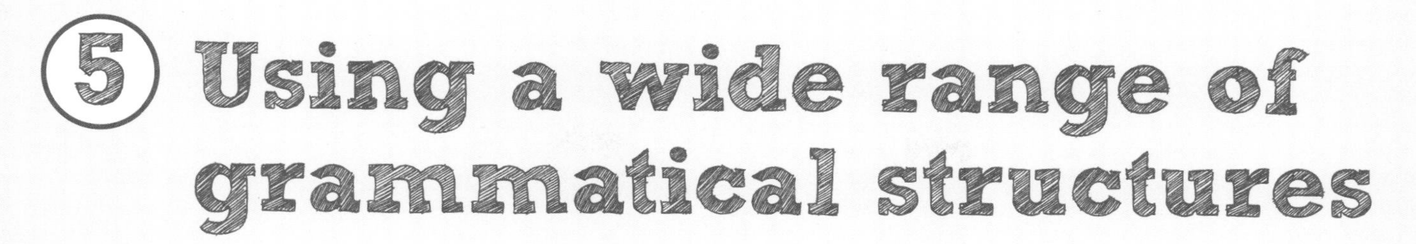

5 Using a wide range of grammatical structures

This unit will help you use a wide range of grammatical structures. The skills you will build are to:

- use subordinate clauses to write more interestingly
- make the best use of object pronouns
- impress with complex grammar.

In the exam, you will be asked to tackle a writing task such as the one below. This unit will prepare you to plan and write your own response to this question, using a wide range of grammatical structures.

Exam-style question

Les vacances

Un magazine français cherche des articles sur les vacances à l'étranger.

Écrivez un article pour recommander vos vacances à l'étranger aux lecteurs.

Vous **devez** faire référence aux points suivants:

- comment vous avez voyagé
- ce que vous avez aimé en vacances
- les aspects négatifs de vos vacances
- vos prochaines vacances.

Justifiez vos idées et vos opinions.
Écrivez 130–150 mots environ **en français**. **(28 marks)**

The three key questions in the **skills boosts** will help you to use a wide range of grammatical structures.

How do I use subordinate clauses to write more interestingly?

How do I make the best use of object pronouns?

How do I impress with complex grammar?

Look at the sample student answer on the next page.

Get started

Read one student's answer to the exam-style question on page 33.

Je viens de découvrir un pays (1) que je ne connaissais pas, la Tunisie, (2) où on parle arabe et français. Nous (3) y sommes allés en avion parce que c'est rapide. Après avoir passé une semaine sur la plage à Djerba, nous avons visité Tunis, la capitale, (4) qui nous a émerveillés. En me promenant dans le souk, j'ai vu des bracelets. Je (5) les ai trouvés jolis et (6) j'en ai acheté trois. Ce qui (7) m'a surprise, par contre, c'est l'insistance de la vendeuse. Elle voulait (8) m'en vendre d'autres et je (9) lui ai dit de (10) me laisser tranquille.

Dans l'ensemble, j'ai aimé la Tunisie et (11) j'en ai gardé de bons souvenirs. Si (12) j'y retournais, je préfèrerais le printemps, quand il fait moins chaud. Mais il faut que je sois patiente, parce que mes parents sont en train de regarder des sites de voyage et l'année prochaine, nous irons probablement en Islande! **Kaycee Brightman**

1 Tick the three statements about Kaycee's holiday in Tunisia that are true.

- **a** She spoke Arabic. ☐
- **b** She stayed in Djerba. ☐
- **c** She thought Tunis was wonderful. ☐
- **d** She walked around in the market. ☐
- **e** She bought half a dozen bangles. ☐
- **f** She enjoyed talking to the shopkeeper. ☐

2 Which word does each highlighted pronoun in Kaycee's text stand for or refer to? Write the correct word from the box below next to each number. You will need to use some of the words more than once.

Example: 1 *un pays* 2 .... 3 .... 4 ....
5 .... 6 .... 7 .... 8 ....
9 .... 10 .... 11 .... 12 ....

les bracelets	Kaycee	un pays	la Tunisie	Tunis	la vendeuse

3 Use structures and phrases from Kaycee's answer to help you fill in the gaps in these translations. The sentences are in the same order as the structures you need in the text.

- **a** She has just spent three days in Italy. – *Elle* .... *passer trois jours en Italie.*
- **b** After shopping, we had lunch. – .... *fait des courses, nous avons déjeuné.*
- **c** By reading a novel, you can relax. – .... *un roman, on peut se détendre.*
- **d** If I went to France, I would visit Paris. – *Si j'allais en France, je* .... *Paris.*
- **e** I must be on time. – *Il faut que* .... *à l'heure.*
- **f** He is in the process of booking a hotel. – *Il est* .... *réserver un hôtel.*

 How do I use subordinate clauses to write more interestingly?

Find opportunities to use different subordinate clauses, which add detail and interest:

- relative clauses with *qui, que, ce qui, ce que*
- clauses with *quand, pendant que, au moment où* to express time.

① Use relative clauses with *qui* or *que* to add extra information to a short sentence. Draw ✎ lines to match each sentence with the missing relative clause.

A La tarte aux pommes de Chez Adèle est un bon dessert, … .	**a** que je choisis souvent
B Nous sommes allés au Café de la Plage, … .	**b** que j'ai recommandé à mes amis
C Nous avons remercié le serveur, Ahmed, … .	**c** qui était trop bruyant
D Le restaurant Moules & Co, … , est la meilleure brasserie de Bruxelles.	**d** qui était très gentil

② Use relative clauses with *qui* and *que/qu'* to define a noun. Complete ✎ the sentences with a relative clause. Use the verb given in brackets.

- *Qui* and *ce qui* are the subject of the verb.
- *Que* and *ce que(qu')* are the object of the verb.

Example: La Suisse est mon pays préféré. (préférer) → La Suisse est le pays *que je préfère.*

a J'ai pris le plat sans viande. (contenir) → J'ai pris le plat ……………………

b Mes parents choisissent les restaurants bien connus. (connaître) → Mes parents choisissent les restaurants ……………………

③ When expressing an opinion, use *ce qui/ce que* at the start of the sentence to add emphasis. Complete ✎ the sentences as in the examples.

Examples: Le saumon fumé coûte cher. → *Ce qui coûte cher, c'est le saumon fumé.*

En Suisse, j'ai aimé la fondue. → *Ce que j'ai aimé en Suisse, c'est la fondue.*

a J'ai apprécié la cuisine locale. ……………………

b La soupe à l'oignon me dégoûte. ……………………

Use subordinate clauses with *quand* (when), *pendant que* (while) or *au moment où* (at the point when) to say **when** something happened:
Quand *nous sommes arrivés au restaurant, il ne restait plus de table.*
Pendant que *nous mangions, un guitariste jouait.*
Au moment où *nous sommes sortis, il a commencé à pleuvoir.*

④ On paper, rewrite ✎ these sentences, using *quand, pendant que* or *au moment où* as appropriate.

a Je faisais du shopping au marché et mes parents écrivaient des cartes postales.

b Nous sommes arrivés à la gare mais le taxi est tombé en panne.

c Au marché de Noël, j'ai mangé des gaufres au sucre.

d Je suis rentré dans le café mais mon téléphone a sonné.

2 How do I make the best use of object pronouns?

Using object pronouns (direct or indirect) and the pronouns *y* and *en* to replace nouns will make your writing sound more convincing. Object pronouns always come before the verb.

1. Look at this student's response to a question about holidays. Find and circle (A) eight more direct object pronouns and link them with the noun or subject pronoun that they replace.

Mon week-end à la montagne avec Sunita a mal commencé! Pourtant, on le préparait depuis longtemps et on l'attendait avec impatience. Mon père m'a déposée à la gare à 8 heures. J'avais rendez-vous avec Sunita mais je ne la voyais pas. Je l'ai appelée, mais pas de réponse. À 8h20, Sunita est arrivée … avec mes chaussures de marche à la main! Je les avais oubliées chez elle. Je l'ai embrassée. Le chef de gare nous a aidées à monter dans le train et on l'a remercié.

Remember that object pronouns always come before the verb.

2. Rewrite sentences a–d using a direct object pronoun. Fill in the gap in e–f.

a J'ai acheté le billet. ....

b Elle retrouve son amie. ....

c Il regarde les horaires. ....

d Elle conduit son frère à l'aéroport. ....

e «Je suis en retard, Maman! Tu .... déposes à la gare?»

f «Notre avion atterrit à midi. Tu viens .... chercher?»

3. Joe's mother asks him whether he's written to friends and family during his holiday. On paper, write Joe's answer to each of his mother's questions.

Example: *À ma grand-mère? Oui, je* ***lui*** *ai écrit. …*

Joe, as-tu écrit à ta grand-mère? À ton grand-père? À tes cousins? Aux voisins? À ton oncle et ta tante? À ta sœur?

Indirect object pronouns are the same as direct object pronouns, except in the third person:

J'ai parlé	à Marie.	*Je **lui** ai parlé.*
	à Thomas.	*Je **lui** ai parlé.*
	à mes amis.	*Je **leur** ai parlé.*

The indirect object pronoun *lui* is both masculine and feminine.

4. Some of the sentences below refer to places and can be rewritten using *y*. Some have *de/des* (or number) + direct object which can be replaced with *en*. Underline (A) the place or circle (A) the direct object, then rewrite the sentences.

a On a passé une nuit au camping.

....

b Elle a mangé beaucoup de pâtisseries.

....

c Nous allons assister au concert.

....

d J'ai aperçu des dauphins.

....

e Ils sont allés à Paris.

....

f J'ai vu deux singes.

....

*Je vais aller **à la boutique de souvenirs**. → Je vais **y** aller.*
*J'ai acheté **des cartes postales**. → J'**en** ai acheté.*
*J'ai pris **deux glaces**. → J'**en** ai pris **deux**.*

3 How do I impress with complex grammar?

Attempts at using more complex French grammar will be rewarded so it is worth practising a few complex structures which are quite different from English.

① Read both versions of the message Jamila wrote to her friend during her trip to Morocco. In text B underline Ⓐ the equivalent phrases for the 11 highlighted phrases in text A.

A

Nous arrivons juste à Essaouira. D'abord, nous sommes allés à l'hôtel, puis nous avons mangé, et nous explorons maintenant la vieille ville. Je t'écris et en même temps, je mange une glace dans un café du souk. J'adore le souk même si c'est très bruyant!

Mes parents discutent en ce moment le prix d'un tagine avec un vendeur. Je crois qu'ils vont l'acheter! Même si ce n'est pas très cher, ils devraient encore négocier. Moi, je dois aller poster ma carte pour ma grand-mère. On va quitter Essaouira demain mais avant, je vais t'envoyer des photos. Je t'embrasse.

B

Nous venons d'arriver à Essaouira. Après être allés à l'hôtel et après avoir mangé, nous explorons maintenant la vieille ville. Je t'écris en mangeant une glace dans un café du souk. J'adore le souk, bien que ce soit très bruyant!

Mes parents sont en train de discuter le prix d'un tagine avec un vendeur. Je crois qu'ils sont sur le point de l'acheter! Bien que ce ne soit pas très cher, ils devraient encore négocier. Moi, il faut que j'aille poster ma carte pour ma grand-mère. Avant de quitter Essaouira demain, je vais t'envoyer des photos. Je t'embrasse.

② Draw lines to match the French structures with their English equivalents.

A *venir de* + infinitive	a after having been somewhere
B *être en train de* + infinitive	b after having done something
C *être sur le point de* + infinitive	c by/while doing something
D *en* + present participle (*-ant*)	d to be just about to do something
E *après avoir* + past participle	e although it is/I am ...
F *après être* + past participle	f I have to go ...
G *avant de* + infinitive	g to have just done something
H *il faut que j'aille ...*	h before doing something
I *bien que ce soit / je sois ...*	i to be in the process of doing something

③ On paper, rewrite Jamila's second message using the structures A–I in ② to replace the underlined phrases.

J'ai juste fini mes bagages et je vais bientôt quitter Agadir. Je vais partir mais, avant, je dois aller dire au revoir à Nader, un jeune Marocain que j'ai rencontré à l'hôtel quand on jouait au tennis. Même si je suis timide, je lui ai parlé. On a joué au tennis tous les jours, puis on est allés à la plage ensemble, et on est devenus amis. Je crois que je tombe amoureuse! À bientôt!

Sample response

This is a writing task of the type you will have to do in the exam. Read Liam's answer below.

Exam-style question

Les vacances à l'hôtel

Un magazine français cherche des articles sur les hôtels.

Écrivez un article pour informer les lecteurs de ce que vous pensez des vacances à l'hôtel.

Vous **devez** faire référence aux points suivants:

- les avantages et les inconvénients de ce genre d'hébergement
- ce que vous appréciez plus particulièrement à l'hôtel
- un séjour que vous avez fait dans un hôtel
- l'hébergement de vacances idéal pour vous.

Justifiez vos idées et vos opinions.

Écrivez environ 130–150 mots **en français**. **(28 marks)**

Les hôtels qui offrent beaucoup d'activités sont très populaires, mais quand ils sont bruyants et sales, c'est l'horreur. En choisissant un hôtel sur Internet, il faut bien lire les avis avant de réserver. Pour moi, un hôtel devrait surtout être un endroit agréable où on peut se relaxer.

Nous venons de faire l'expérience d'un hôtel abominable! Nous l'avions réservé après avoir lu des avis positifs. Bien que je ne sois pas exigeant, j'ai trouvé ma chambre horriblement sale. On y a trouvé des insectes, ce qui m'a choqué. Le directeur n'a pas été sympa quand nous lui en avons parlé. Tout était horrible dans cet hôtel: je ne le recommanderai certainement pas!

Si je pouvais, je n'irais plus à l'hôtel. Ce que je préférerais, c'est camper! Si j'ai assez d'argent l'année prochaine, je ferai du camping à la campagne avec des copains. Ce sera très sympa!

1 Has Liam followed the advice and used a wide range of grammatical structures? Complete the table with at least one example from his text in each box.

relative clauses using *qui, que, où, ce qui* or *ce que*	
other subordinate clauses (using *quand*, etc.)	
sentences using *si* (present/future; imperfect/conditional)	
direct object pronouns	
indirect object pronouns	
pronouns *y* and *en*	
complex structures, e.g. verbal phrase + *de* + infinitive	
en + present participle	
après être/avoir + past participle	
avant de + infinitive	
special phrase + subjunctive	

Your turn!

You are now going to plan and write your response to the exam-style question from page 33.

1. First jot down your ideas in French, concentrating on relevant details for each bullet point.

   How you travelled ....

   What you liked about the holiday ....

   Good points of a holiday abroad ....

   What was bad? / went wrong? ....

   Bad points of a holiday abroad ....

   Plans for your next holiday ....

   Would you go back to the same place? Why?

2. Write your answer to the exam-style question. Then check your work with the checklist.

Learn these phrases by heart. They contain object pronouns or *y* or *en* and are easy to reuse:

ça me plaît – I enjoy it

ça m'a plu – I enjoyed it

ce qui m'inquiète, c'est ... – what worries me is ...

ce qui m'inquiétait, c'était ... – what I found worrying was ...

j'y vais souvent – I often go there

je n'en ai pas envie – I don't feel like it, I don't like it

Checklist **In my answer do I ...**	✓
use relative clauses?	
use other subordinate clauses?	
use *si* sentences? *si* + present + future *si* + imperfect + conditional	
use direct object and indirect object pronouns?	
use the pronouns *y* and *en*?	
use a complex structure?	

Review your skills

Check up

Review your response to the exam-style question on page 39. Tick the column to show how well you think you have done each of the following.

	Not quite	Nearly there	Got it!
used subordinate clauses to write more interestingly	☐	☐	☐
made the best use of object pronouns	☐	☐	☐
used complex grammatical structures	☐	☐	☐

Need more practice?

On paper, plan and write your response to the exam-style question below.

Exam-style question

Un mail

Votre correspondant(e) vous demande votre avis sur les vacances en famille.

Écrivez un mail pour l'informer de ce que vous pensez de ce genre de vacances.

Vous **devez** faire référence aux points suivants:

- les bons côtés des vacances en famille
- ce que vous n'aimez pas
- des vacances catastrophiques avec votre famille
- vos rêves pour les prochaines vacances.

Justifiez vos idées et vos opinions. Écrivez environ 130–150 mots **en français**. (28 marks)

Salut!

...

To write a good answer in the long writing task you need to:

- include lots of interesting content
- communicate your ideas clearly
- give opinions and justify them
- use verbs in different tenses accurately
- use complex sentences
- use a variety of connectives
- make use of pronouns
- attempt complex grammatical structures.

il faut que [...] and *bien que* [...] are followed by the subjunctive. Try to memorise these:

je vais → *il faut que j'aille*

je (ne) suis (pas) → *bien que je (ne) sois (pas)*

c'est/ce n'est pas → *bien que ce (ne) soit (pas)*

How confident do you feel about each of these **skills**? Colour in the bars.

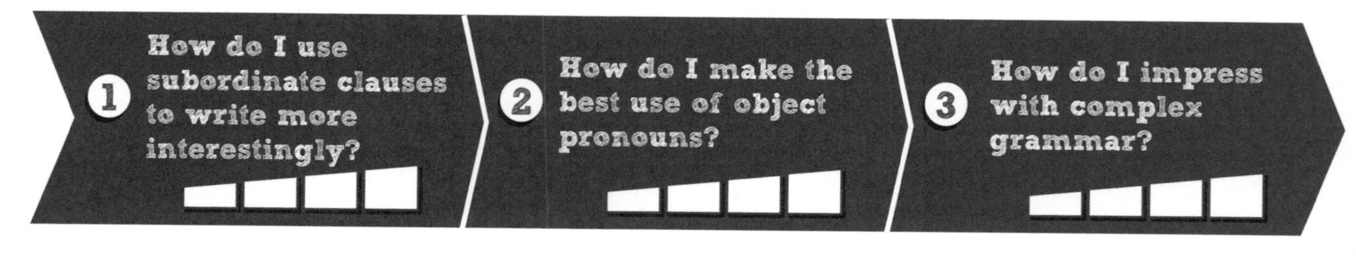

Maintaining the reader's interest

This unit will help you keep your readers interested. The skills you will build are to:

- vary the length of your sentences
- use linking words such as *en plus* (moreover), *malgré* (in spite of), etc. effectively
- write in an engaging and original way.

In the exam, you will be asked to tackle a writing task such as the one below. This unit will prepare you to plan and write a response to this question that will maintain the reader's interest.

Exam-style question

Échange scolaire

Votre collège voudrait commencer un échange scolaire avec le collège français Louis Pasteur.

Écrivez une lettre au directeur de Louis Pasteur pour décrire ce qui est intéressant dans votre collège.

Vous **devez** faire référence aux points suivants:

- pourquoi vous voulez faire un échange scolaire
- pourquoi votre collège est un bon collège
- une occasion mémorable dans votre collège
- un projet scolaire.

Justifiez vos idées et vos opinions.
Écrivez 130–150 mots environ **en français**. (28 marks)

The three key questions in the **skills boosts** will help you to maintain the reader's interest.

How do I vary the length of my sentences?

How do I use linking words effectively?

How do I write in an engaging and original way?

Look at the sample student answer on the next page.

Get started

Read one student's answer to the exam-style question on page 41.

> *Il me semble que mon collège devrait faire davantage d'échanges scolaires, qui sont une bonne façon de découvrir une autre culture, surtout quand on apprend une langue étrangère.*
>
> *Je trouve que mon collège, Hillview, est une école dynamique. D'abord, les installations sportives, qui comprennent une salle multisports, sont excellentes. En plus, le CDI, bien qu'il ne soit pas très grand, est équipé non seulement en livres, mais aussi en matériel informatique moderne.*
>
> *Grâce à ce matériel, le mois dernier, ma classe a participé à une vidéoconférence que le professeur de géographie avait organisée avec le collège Kenyatta à Nairobi. Au lieu d'envoyer des mails individuels, comme nous le faisions auparavant, nous avons travaillé ensemble malgré la distance. Nous avons trouvé que c'était une expérience extraordinaire et par conséquent, nous allons bientôt mettre en place un autre échange virtuel avec un collège au Pakistan. J'espère qu'un échange intéressera aussi les collégiens de Louis Pasteur.* **Rubina**

1 i Which of these statements about Rubina's answer are true? Write T (true) or F (false) in each box.

ii Then cross out ~~cat~~ the incorrect information in the false statements and write the correct information on the line.

a Rubina thinks learning a foreign language is more important than doing a school exchange. ☐

....

b She says there aren't enough books in the school library. ☐

....

c Rubina's class has been able to speak to students in Africa. ☐

....

d Recently, they stopped exchanging emails with the African students. ☐

....

e The European and African students worked together in spite of language problems. ☐

....

f Rubina's classmates enjoyed the experience. ☐

....

g They would rather set up an exchange with a school in Pakistan than with Louis Pasteur. ☐ ....

2 In these two long sentences from Rubina's answer:

a find and underline two subordinate clauses

b find and circle three other linking words

> A subordinate clause adds information to a sentence and is introduced by a connective such as *parce que, quand* ... or a relative pronoun such as *qui.*

> *En plus, le CDI, bien qu'il ne soit pas très grand, est équipé non seulement en livres, mais aussi en matériel informatique.*
>
> *Au lieu d'envoyer des mails individuels, comme nous le faisions auparavant, nous avons travaillé ensemble malgré la distance.*

3 In your opinion, what is the most interesting and original thing in Rubina's answer? Copy it here.

....

How do I vary the length of my sentences?

Learn to vary the length of your sentences. Keep some short but build up others, using subordinate clauses.

(1) Extend each sentence about Fred's stay with his exchange partner, Tom, by selecting a subordinate clause from the list on the right. Write each letter in the correct box.

A À l'arrivée, je suis allé chez les parents de Tom [h].	**a** qui était un mercredi,
B Dans le jardin, [ ] j'ai fait la connaissance de son chien Bruno.	**b** comme Tom fait du judo après les cours,
C J'ai envoyé un texto à mes parents [ ].	**c** pour donner des nouvelles
D Le premier jour de l'échange, [ ] j'ai pris le bus avec Tom pour aller au collège.	**d** ce que j'ai apprécié bien plus que l'accrobranche
E Le jeudi soir, [ ] je suis rentré seul du collège.	**e** depuis que je suis arrivé,
F Le samedi, on a fait de l'accrobranche mais je n'ai pas aimé ça [ ].	**f** pendant que Tom sortait mes bagages de la voiture,
G Le dimanche, on a visité une biscuiterie [ ].	**g** , parce que j'avais peur de tomber
H Les parents de Tom sont très gentils et [ ] je ne me suis jamais ennuyé.	**h** , qui sont venus me chercher à la gare

(2) Circle the connective or relative pronoun at the start of each subordinate clause in the right-hand column in (1). Beware: they are sometimes made up of two words, e.g. *ce que*.

(3) Extend these short sentences on paper using the prompts given in brackets and words from the box. Use at least one different way for each one. There is more than one possible answer.

comme	depuis que	je pense que	parce que
pour + *infinitive*	puisque	qui/que	

Include subordinate clauses starting with:
parce que – because
puisque – since
pendant que – while
depuis que – since
bien que – although
je pense que – I think that
il/elle dit que – he/she says that

You can also link two clauses with:
car – because
pour + infinitive – in order to

Example: Nous sommes allés à Limoges en car. (avion très cher)
Comme l'avion est très cher, nous sommes allés à Limoges en car.

a Nous sommes arrivés à minuit. (circulation sur l'autoroute)

b Les parents de Morgane sont très sympa. (opinion)

c Leur maison est confortable. (maison: petite mais au centre-ville)

d J'ai demandé le code wifi. (envoyer un message)

e J'ai partagé la chambre de Morgane. (Morgane a deux sœurs)

Impress by using *bien que* (although) + *être* or *faire* in the subjunctive:
- *elle n'**est** pas grande* → ***bien qu'**elle ne **soit** pas grande, …* (although it isn't large, …)
- *il **fait** froid* → ***bien qu'**il **fasse** froid, …* (although the weather is cold, …).

(4) On paper, write two sentences explaining what you liked best on your last holiday abroad. Start with short sentences, then extend each one using one or two subordinate clauses.

2 How do I use linking words effectively?

Extend your sentences with linking words by spotting opportunities such as:
- adding examples or arguments with *en plus, c'est-à-dire ...*
- highlighting a contradiction with *cependant, malgré ...*

Grâce à (thanks to) introduces something positive.
À cause de (because of) introduces something negative.

1. Read the sentences and look at the linking words in bold. Circle (A) those that add an example or supporting argument and underline (A) those that introduce a contrast or contradiction.

   a Je déteste mon uniforme, **même si** le blazer est élégant.

   b Le règlement du collège est strict et **d'ailleurs**, les élèves protestent.

   c Mon uniforme comprend un pantalon, une chemise, un blazer, **sans oublier** la cravate bleue.

   d **Non seulement** les cours commencent tôt, **mais en plus** ils finissent tard, à 17 heures.

   e L'été, **au lieu de** prendre le car, je vais au collège à vélo.

   f **Grâce aux** grandes vacances, on peut bien se reposer l'été.

   g J'ai cours tous les jours du lundi au samedi, **sauf** le mercredi après-midi.

   h **Malgré** le règlement, beaucoup d'élèves ont des piercings.

   i Si on a de mauvaises notes, il est fréquent de redoubler, **c'est-à-dire** de rester dans la même classe.

   j On n'a pas le droit de quitter le collège **sans** permission.

2. Copy each linking word from 1 next to the correct English equivalent.

Example or argument		Contrast or contradiction	
as it happens		instead of	
not forgetting		even if	
thanks to		in spite of	
not only ... but also		without	
that is to say		except	

3. Decide if the second sentence in each pair provides an example or a contrast. On paper, rewrite each pair as one extended sentence, using a suitable linking word from the table in 2.

   a Les vacances scolaires sont longues. On travaille dur à l'école en France.

   b Il n'y a que 150 élèves dans mon collège. Les équipements sont très modernes.

   c Comme matières obligatoires, j'ai français, anglais, histoire-géo et SVT. J'étudie aussi les maths et la physique.

   d Quelquefois, on manque les cours. On va à la cafétéria du centre commercial.

   e Dans certains villages du Burkina Faso, il y a des connexions Internet. On peut étudier à distance.

   f J'aime les matières littéraires. J'aime le français, l'anglais, l'histoire et l'allemand.

3 How do I write in an engaging and original way?

Add some sparkle by mentioning unusual aspects of the topic you are given to write about. Think outside the box and identify ways of coming up with less predictable answers. Try writing about different **actions**, **places**, **time frames** and **people**, as well as adding **specific examples** to general statements.

Topic: Que pensez-vous du collège?					
Plain, predictable answers ↓	**Different ...**				**Specific examples**
	actions	**places**	**time frames**	**people**	
A Au collège, j'aime surtout les langues.	1	2	3	4	5
B Je n'aime pas les matières scientifiques.	6	7	8	9	10
C J'ai de bons copains.	11	12	13	14	15
D Les équipements sont insuffisants.	16	17	18	19	20
E La plupart des profs sont sympa.	21	22	23	24	25
F On ne fait pas assez de sorties scolaires.	26	27	28	29	30

1 The statements below are more interesting alternatives to sentence A. Number them according to where they belong in Row A in the matrix, based on the underlined text.

Example: [4] J'ai deux correspondants: Nico est allemand et Liu est chinoise.

a [ ] En plus des cours, je révise le vocabulaire avec des applis sur mon smartphone.

b [ ] Non seulement je fais du français, mais j'étudie l'allemand et j'ai commencé le mandarin.

c [ ] L'année prochaine, nous allons faire un échange avec un collège allemand.

d [ ] Mon meilleur souvenir, c'est un voyage scolaire à Berlin en hiver, sous la neige.

2 Use the prompts below to write full sentences. Number them according to where they belong in Row B in the matrix.

a [10] maths 😐; physique ☹; chimie ☹ ☹

....

b [ ] laboratoire de chimie, très ancien, froid l'hiver

....

c [ ] copain Pablo: fort en maths, prêt à aider

....

d [ ] rater les cours; avoir de mauvaises notes

....

e [ ] année prochaine: arrêter les sciences; faire un effort + continuer les maths

....

3 On paper, write 10 statements to match any 10 cells between 11 and 30 in the matrix. Make them as interesting as you can.

Remember: this is about showing your ability to write good French, not about telling the truth. For example, if you only have lukewarm feelings about school, be creative and imagine some interesting situations.

Sample response

Now look at this exam-style writing task, similar to the one you saw on page 41.

Exam-style question

Le règlement de notre collège

Vos correspondants du collège Saint-Laurent au Québec viennent passer un mois au Royaume-Uni. Écrivez un message sur le forum du collège Saint-Laurent pour donner des informations sur le règlement de votre collège.

Vous **devez** faire référence aux points suivants:

- les règles principales
- pourquoi il est important de les respecter
- un incident lié au règlement
- comment le règlement va évoluer à l'avenir.

Justifiez vos idées et vos opinions. Écrivez 130–150 mots environ **en français**. **(28 marks)**

Voici les règles principales. Non seulement il faut arriver à l'heure, mais il est aussi interdit de manquer les cours sans raison, ce qui est normal, je pense. En plus, on est obligés de laisser notre portable dans des casiers qui sont sécurisés grâce à un mot de passe. C'est important pour éviter les distractions en cours.

La règle la plus surprenante pour vous, ce sera probablement l'uniforme scolaire, que tous les élèves sans exception doivent porter. Par contre, les visiteurs comme vous peuvent venir en sweat bleu au lieu de l'uniforme complet.

L'année dernière, pendant «mufti», c'est-à-dire la journée où les élèves portent ce qu'ils veulent, la plupart des élèves étaient en jean. Il y a une fille, par contre, qui est venue déguisée en clown et malgré ses excuses, le directeur l'a renvoyée chez elle. À cause de cet incident, il n'y aura plus de journée «mufti» et le règlement va devenir plus strict. Nathan

1. Identify the four longest sentences in Nathan's answer. Underline (A) the subordinate clauses and circle (A) the linking words used to extend these sentences.
2. Find all the linking words that introduce an example or an argument and a contrast or a contradiction. Copy each word in the correct column.

Introducing an example/ argument:		Introducing a contrast/ contradiction:
....	....	....
....	....	....
....	....	....
		....

3. Find and copy one example of how Nathan uses each of the following to add interest.

   Different actions: ....

   Different places: ....

   Different time frames: ....

   Different people: ....

   Specific examples: ....
4. Note down what you think is the most unusual or original thing Nathan says in his email.

   ....

Your turn!

You are now going to plan and write your response to the exam-style question from page 41.

Exam-style question

Échange scolaire

Votre collège voudrait commencer un échange scolaire avec le collège français Louis Pasteur.

Écrivez une lettre au directeur de Louis Pasteur pour décrire ce qui est intéressant dans votre collège.

Vous **devez** faire référence aux points suivants:

1. Look back at the bullet points on page 41. First jot down your ideas in French.

   Why you want to do a school exchange

   Positive points about your school

   A memorable occasion at school

   A future plan or project (real or invented)

2. Write your answer to the exam-style question. Then check your work with the checklist.

Checklist In my answer do I ...	✓
answer all four bullet points?	
express clear opinions?	
give justifications for my opinions?	
refer to various time frames (past, present, future)?	
vary the length of my sentences, using subordinate clauses?	
use a variety of linking words?	
include original and unusual information?	

Review your skills

Check up

Review your response to the exam-style question on page 47. Tick the column to show how well you think you have done each of the following.

	Not quite	Nearly there	Got it!
varied the length of my sentences			
used linking words effectively			
written in an engaging and original way			

Need more practice?

On paper, plan and write your response to the exam-style question below.

Exam-style question

Profiter du collège

Écrivez un message dans un forum francophone pour convaincre les lecteurs de profiter au maximum de leurs années d'école.

Vous **devez** faire référence aux points suivants:

- ce qu'on peut faire au collège en dehors des cours
- pourquoi ces activités sont importantes
- vos meilleures expériences au collège cette année
- les activités extrascolaires que vous allez faire plus tard au lycée.

Justifiez vos idées et vos opinions.

Écrivez 130–150 mots environ **en français**. **(28 marks)**

To write a good answer, try to include:

- a clear message, even if some errors slip in
- detailed information
- varied vocabulary and structures to interest, inform or convince the reader
- many examples of uncommon language
- varied grammatical structures, including complex ones
- creative language use to express individual ideas and points of view
- extended, well-linked sentences
- references to past, present and future events
- formal style and register.

How confident do you feel about each of these skills? Colour in the bars.

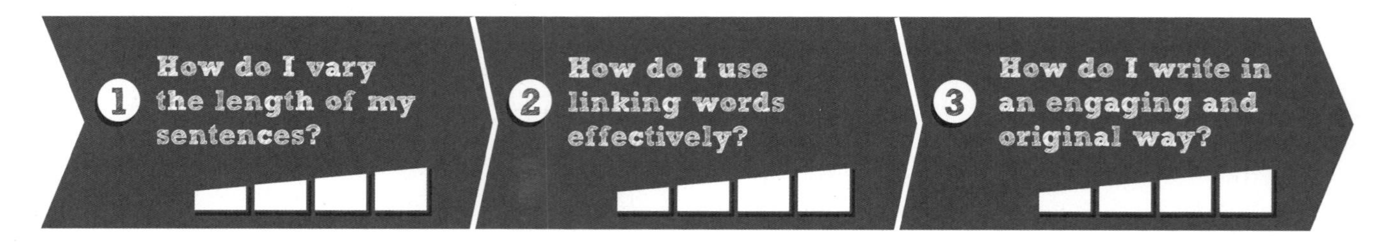

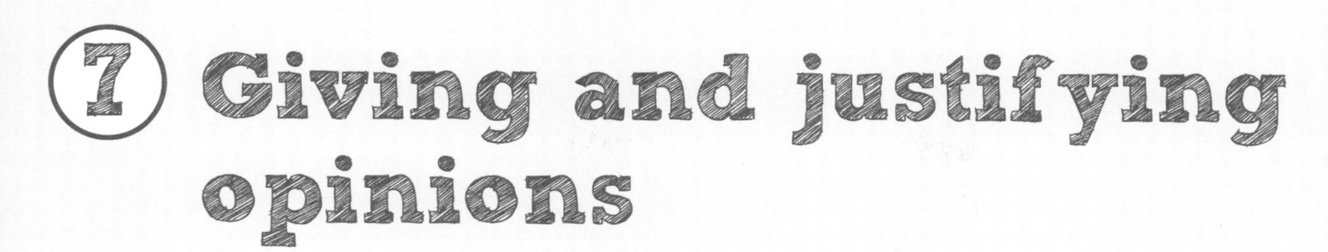

7 Giving and justifying opinions

This unit will help you learn to express opinions and justify them convincingly. The skills you will build are to:

- use all opportunities to express opinions
- justify your opinions
- justify your opinions convincingly.

In the exam, you will be asked to tackle writing tasks such as the one below. This unit will prepare you to plan and write your own response to this question. You will be paying particular attention to giving opinions, which is one of the requirements for answering both the short and long writing tasks.

Exam-style question

Un stage

Vous voulez faire un stage comme réceptionniste dans un hôtel en France.

Écrivez une lettre au directeur de l'hôtel pour le convaincre de vous prendre.

Vous **devez** faire référence aux points suivants:

- vos qualités pour le poste
- les langues que vous parlez
- un stage que vous avez déjà fait
- l'importance de faire un stage.

Justifiez vos réponses et vos opinions.
Écrivez 130–150 mots environ **en français**. **(28 marks)**

Monsieur le directeur,

...

The three key questions in the **skills boosts** will help you give your opinions convincingly.

How do I use all opportunities to express opinions?

How do I justify my opinions?

How do I justify my opinions convincingly?

Look at the sample student answer on the next page.

Get started

Read one student's answer to the exam-style question on page 49.

Monsieur le directeur,

Je crois avoir les qualités nécessaires pour faire ce stage car non seulement j'apprécie le contact avec le public mais je suis aussi travailleuse, ponctuelle et motivée.

En plus, j'ai la chance de parler plusieurs langues: l'anglais, le français, que j'apprends depuis 10 ans, et l'espagnol, ce qui sera utile dans votre hôtel.

J'ai de l'expérience: j'ai effectivement fait un stage formidable dans un camping l'été dernier. Ce qui m'a beaucoup plu, c'était accueillir les visiteurs. Je pense que la directrice était très contente de mon travail puisqu'elle m'a proposé un job pour l'été prochain.

J'estime que faire un stage est essentiel pour découvrir un métier et je suis persuadée que cela me donne l'expérience qui m'aidera à trouver plus facilement un emploi après les études. Malheureusement, ce n'est pas toujours facile de trouver des stages et à mon avis, le travail qu'on nous demande de faire n'est pas toujours intéressant.

1. Beth gives six reasons why she's the right person for the job. Note down what they are in English.

 ....
 ....
 ....

2. Circle the correct word(s) in these statements about some of Beth's opinions.

 a. Beth **thinks / doesn't think** she's got the qualities needed for the job.
 b. She **likes / doesn't like** working with the public.
 c. She **liked / didn't like** her previous work experience placement.
 d. She believes work experience **helps / doesn't help** you to find out what a job is like.
 e. According to her, work experience **will help / won't help** her to find a job later.
 f. She thinks it **is / is not** easy to find a work experience placement.
 g. She believes the type of work you do on a work experience placement **is / is not** always interesting.

3. Read the text again. Beth has introduced her opinions in different ways. Find and note down the French for these phrases.

 I believe .... I am convinced ....
 I think .... in my opinion ....
 I feel/I reckon ....

4. How else did Beth express her opinions? Find and note down the following:

 I enjoy ....
 I am lucky enough to ....
 What I really liked ....

How do I use all opportunities to express opinions?

When you give opinions, try to avoid always using *Je pense que* and try to go beyond adding *c'est/c'était super or c'est/c'était nul!* Instead, write as many sentences as possible that:

- use adjectives, adverbs and verbs that clearly indicate your view
- use expressions of interest, likes and dislikes.

① Read George's answer to the question: *Racontez un stage.* He started by writing the sentences on the left giving information about his work experience placement. On the right, he improved his sentences in order to indicate his opinion. Now complete the following steps for a–i below.

i Write P (positive) or N (negative) in the box next to each sentence.

ii Underline the words in the second column which are used to give an opinion (adjective, adverb, verb, like/dislike, etc.).

a	J'ai fait un stage chez un vétérinaire.	J'ai fait un stage formidable chez un vétérinaire.	
b	J'ai fait du café.	Ce qui ne m'a pas plu pendant le stage, c'était faire le café.	
c	J'ai répondu au téléphone.	Je n'ai pas aimé répondre au téléphone.	
d	J'ai observé les vétérinaires.	Le plus passionnant, c'était observer les vétérinaires.	
e	Je me suis occupé des animaux dans l'infirmerie.	J'ai adoré m'occuper des animaux dans l'infirmerie.	
f	J'ai manipulé des animaux très malades.	J'ai trouvé difficile de manipuler les animaux très malades.	
g	J'ai parlé à leurs propriétaires.	Ça m'a beaucoup stressé de parler à leurs propriétaires.	
h	Les infirmières étaient toujours là.	Heureusement, les infirmières étaient toujours là.	
i	Je vais faire un autre stage chez un véto.	Je rêve de faire un autre stage chez un véto.	

② On paper, rewrite each of George's sentences to say exactly the opposite, using the words and phrases below appropriately.

adjectives:	*horrible; le moins intéressant*
adverbs:	*malheureusement*
verbs:	*j'ai bien aimé; J'ai détesté; J'ai trouvé très facile de*
phrases:	*ça ne m'a pas dérangé(e) de; ce qui m'a plu; je n'ai pas envie de*

2 How do I justify my opinions?

Always try to explain or justify your opinion but avoid saying *parce que* or *car* every time! You have learned a variety of connectives (see pages 4, 13 and 43) and using them in your writing will impress.

1 **a** Draw lines to match up the sentence halves in a way that makes sense to answer the question: *À votre avis, quel est le métier pour vous?*

b Fill the gaps with an appropriate connective from the box.

comme (*as*)	en effet (*indeed, in fact*)	grâce à/au/aux (*thanks to*)
puisque (*as, since*)	non seulement … mais de plus (*not only … but also*)	
par exemple … ou bien (*for example … or alternatively*)		

A J'estime que le meilleur métier pour moi, c'est médecin:

B Je pense que le secteur qui m'attire le plus, c'est le commerce

C Moi, mon ambition serait de devenir golfeur professionnel

D Je crois que ça m'intéresserait de travailler dans les arts.

E Personnellement, je sais déjà que je veux travailler dans le secteur du tourisme

F Le plus important pour moi, c'est de faire un travail bien payé,

a ………………… j'adore travailler dans le magasin de mes parents.

b …………………, au collège, je m'intéresse surtout à la musique, au théâtre et au dessin.

c ………………… j'aime la biologie ………………… je voudrais aider les gens.

d ………………… stages que j'ai faits et adorés dans des agences de voyage.

e ………………… le métier de banquier ………………… celui de comptable.

f ………………… je suis déjà champion régional.

2 Look at the notes below that students have made to answer the question *Une année sabbatique, c'est une bonne idée?* On paper, write complete sentences to give each opinion **and** a justification. Use a different phrase to introduce each opinion and an interesting connective.

Example: très utile / introduction au monde du travail

Pour moi/À mon avis/Selon moi*, une année sabbatique, c'est très utile* ***puisque/comme/parce que*** *c'est une bonne introduction au monde du travail.*

a *essentiel / apprendre à être autonome*

b *mauvaise idée / cher + perte de temps*

c *très important / expérience enrichissante*

d *j'adorerais …! / faire un grand voyage ou faire du bénévolat*

e *pas bénéfique / plus important de finir ses études*

Remember: justifying your opinion can be an opportunity to write extended sentences, using different tenses and complex structures.

How do I justify my opinions convincingly?

To give a convincing justification, you need to be coherent. Make sure you avoid possible contradiction or ambiguity by selecting appropriate ideas and using suitable connectives to introduce extra information, a supporting argument or a contrasting idea.

1 The grid below provides you with a framework for justifying opinions convincingly. It contains some possible answers to the question: *Que pensez-vous de votre petit boulot?*

There are several possible combinations. Pay attention to punctuation when making your choices.

a Choose an element from each column to justify each of the six opinions in the first column. Write the number of each opinion in the appropriate boxes.

b Write out each complete opinion and justification on paper.

Example: *J'aime bien mon job parce qu'il est intéressant et stimulant. Par contre, ce n'est pas bien payé.*

Opinion	Justification	Connective	Logical conclusion
1 J'aime bien mon job	car je m'ennuie beaucoup. [ ]	Malheureusement, [ ]	ce n'est pas bien payé. [1]
2 Je ne trouve pas mon petit boulot super	comme il est bien payé. [ ]	Par contre, [1]	comme il n'y a rien à faire, je m'ennuie. [ ]
3 J'adore mon petit boulot.	puisqu'il est mal payé. [ ]	Cependant, [ ]	c'est très physique et très fatigant. [ ]
4 Mon petit job me plaît assez,	non seulement les horaires sont longs mais c'est aussi loin de chez moi. [ ]	Heureusement, [ ]	j'apprends beaucoup de choses sur le monde du travail. [ ]
5 Mon job est affreux:	En effet, c'est une bonne expérience pour plus tard. [ ]	En plus, [ ]	je suis bien payé. [ ]
6 Je déteste mon job	parce qu'il est intéressant et stimulant. [1]	En plus [ ]	j'apprécie mon patron qui est très sympa. [ ]

2 The grid below contains some incomplete answers to the question: *Que pensez-vous de votre stage?* Add a justification for each opinion in column 2. Then add a logical sentence ending in column 4 which follows on coherently from the connective given in column 3.

Opinion	Justification	Connective	Logical conclusion
a J'ai fait un stage fantastique		Malheureusement,	
b J'ai appris beaucoup de choses		En plus,	
c Je me suis passionné(e) pour le travail		Par contre,	

Sample response

This is a writing task of the type you will have to do in the exam. Read Naseem's answer below.

Exam-style question

Un magazine français cherche des articles sur les jeunes et les petits boulots.

Écrivez un article pour convaincre les lecteurs de trouver un petit boulot.

Vous **devez** faire référence aux points suivants:

- un petit boulot que vous avez eu
- votre prochain petit boulot
- les avantages et les inconvénients d'avoir un petit boulot
- votre carrière de rêve.

Justifiez vos réponses et vos opinions. Écrivez 130–150 mots environ **en français**. **(28 marks)**

L'été dernier, j'ai adoré travailler dans le magasin de ma cousine. C'était passionnant car il y avait beaucoup de clients. Ce qui m'a plu le plus, c'était parler français avec les touristes puisque je révisais mon vocabulaire!

L'été prochain, si je pouvais, j'aimerais travailler à l'office de tourisme parce que je m'intéresse beaucoup à ce secteur, mais, si ce n'est pas possible, ça ne me dérangerait pas de retravailler avec ma cousine.

Grâce à un petit boulot, on peut gagner de l'argent de poche, ce que je trouve important. En plus, j'estime que c'est une excellente façon d'obtenir une expérience professionnelle.

Malheureusement, mes parents sont contre et pensent qu'un job n'est pas utile. Selon eux, il faut se concentrer d'abord sur les études.

Mon métier idéal serait professeur parce que j'adore les enfants. En plus, je crois avoir les qualités nécessaires: en effet, je suis sociable et j'ai beaucoup de patience!

1 Has Naseem followed the advice and given opinions and justified them convincingly? Complete the table with examples from the text.

phrases introducing an opinion	*je trouve*
adjectives that imply an opinion	
adverbs that imply an opinion	
verbs that imply an opinion	
expressions of interest, likes and dislikes	
suitable connectives to explain an opinion	
suitable connectives to add a supporting argument	
suitable connectives to introduce a contrast	

Your turn!

You are now going to plan and write your response to the exam-style question from page 49.

Exam-style question

Un stage

Vous voulez faire un stage comme réceptionniste dans un hôtel en France.
Écrivez une lettre au directeur de l'hôtel pour le convaincre de vous prendre.
Vous **devez** faire référence aux points suivants:

1. Look back at the bullet points on page 49. First jot down your ideas in French, concentrating on giving opinions.

   Your relevant qualities for the post:

   Why they are good qualities for the post:

   Justify your opinion with an example:

   Languages you speak + relevance for the job:

   Work experience placement you have done:

   Opinion of the placement + justification:

   Opinion on the value of work experience:

2. Write your answer to the exam-style question. Then check your work with the checklist.

Checklist In my answer do I …	✓
use a variety of phrases to introduce my opinion?	
use adjectives that indicate my opinion?	
use adverbs that indicate my opinion?	
use verbs that indicate my opinion?	
use expressions of interest, likes and dislikes?	
justify my opinions convincingly?	
use suitable connectives, e.g. to add a supporting argument; to introduce a contrast?	

Review your skills

Check up

Review your response to the exam-style question on page 55. Tick ✓ the column to show how well you think you have done each of the following.

	Not quite ✓	Nearly there ✓	Got it! ✓
used all opportunities to express opinions			
justified my opinions			
Justified my opinions convincingly			

Need more practice?

On paper, plan and write ✎ your response to the exam-style question below.

Exam-style question

Un magazine français cherche des articles sur les jeunes et leurs ambitions dans la vie.

Écrivez un article pour intéresser les lecteurs.

Vous **devez** faire référence aux points suivants:

- vos qualités pour le métier que vous aimeriez faire
- ce que vous voulez absolument faire avant de travailler
- les avantages et les inconvénients d'une année sabbatique
- votre situation de famille idéale dans 30 ans.

Justifiez vos réponses et vos opinions. Écrivez 130–150 mots environ **en français**. **(28 marks)**

To give your opinion fully, remember **IORC**:

Information – must be relevant to what is being discussed

Opinion – decide: agree or disagree? for or against? positive or negative?

Reason – explain why you think that and justify

Contrast – look at the other side of the argument: the pros or the cons

To write a good answer in the long writing task you need to:

- give information addressing all bullet points
- expand key points and ideas
- give convincing personal opinions
- express thoughts, feelings and emotions about relevant issues
- justify your opinions, using appropriate arguments
- write clearly and coherently, avoiding ambiguity
- convince and maintain the reader's interest
- write complex sentences using appropriate connectives
- refer to three different time frames
- use the appropriate style and register.

How confident do you feel about each of these **skills**? Colour in ✎ the bars.

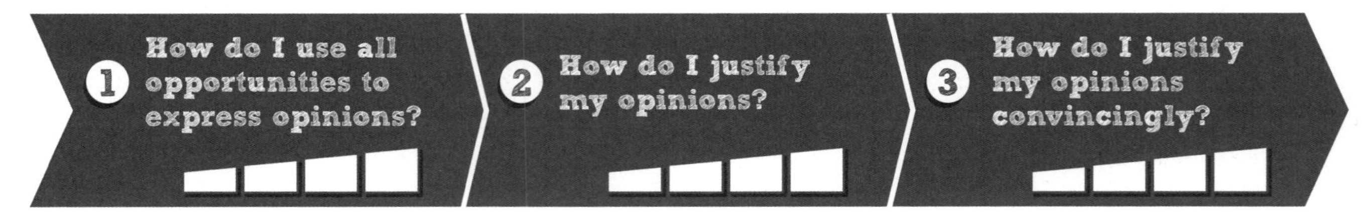

Maintaining accuracy

This unit will help you maintain accuracy in complex language. The skills you will build are to:

- be aware of words that must be included in French, but not in English
- use correct verb forms
- put object pronouns in the correct place and in the right order.

In the exam, you will be asked to tackle a writing task such as the one below. This unit will prepare you to plan and write your own response, in which you will try to remain accurate even when using complex language.

Exam-style question

Notre environnement

Un magazine français cherche des articles sur l'environnement.

Écrivez au magazine pour expliquer pourquoi les problèmes d'environnement inquiètent les jeunes.

Vous **devez** faire référence aux points suivants:

- les problèmes qui vous inquiètent le plus
- pourquoi l'environnement est important pour les jeunes
- ce que vous avez fait pour la protection de l'environnement
- vos idées pour protéger l'environnement.

Justifiez vos idées et vos opinions.

Écrivez 130–150 mots environ **en français**. **(28 marks)**

The three key questions in the **skills boosts** will help you to maintain accuracy in complex language.

How do I watch out for words that have to be included in French?

How do I use correct verb forms?

How do I put object pronouns in the correct place and in the right order?

Look at the sample student answer on the next page.

Read one student's answer to the exam-style question on page 57.

Le niveau de la mer qui monte, cela nous concerne tous. Je pense aussi que la pollution des océans, c'est scandaleux. Bien qu'on fasse des efforts pour ne pas utiliser de plastique, il y en a encore qui est jeté à la mer, où il tue les dauphins parce qu'ils le prennent pour de la nourriture.

Ces questions sont importantes pour les jeunes parce que c'est notre génération qui va en souffrir. Dans notre ville, si la mer continue à monter, il n'y aura bientôt plus de route.

Comme j'habite près de la plage, j'y vais souvent avec mes amis pour la nettoyer en ramassant les déchets. La déchèterie nous a donné des sacs et nous avons trié les canettes en aluminium. La déchèterie nous les a ensuite rachetées, ce qui nous a étonnés mais nous étions contents!

Bientôt, nous allons placer des panneaux pour encourager les gens à emporter leurs canettes et à les recycler.

Olivia

1. Read Olivia's answer above. In each statement below, there are **one** or **two** correct answers. Circle them.

   a. Olivia is concerned by **rising sea levels / dwindling fish stocks / dirty seas.**
   b. People **have stopped using plastic / try to limit their use of plastic / throw away plastic.**
   c. Dolphins **are killed for food / cannot find food / think plastic is food.**
   d. Environmental problems will mostly impact **people her age / older people / fishermen.**
   e. Olivia and her friends **help clean the beach / collect litter / bring their own bags.**
   f. Workers at the rubbish dump **recycle bags / sort aluminium cans / pay the volunteers.**
   g. Next time, Olivia and her friends will **put up information signs / talk to people / collect cans for recycling.**

2. To maintain accuracy, you have to pay attention to detail.

   In Olivia's answer, find and underline the French equivalent of these phrases, then note letters a–g in the correct column in the grid below. (Some can be noted in two of the columns.)

   a. it concerns us all
   b. I also think that pollution of the oceans is scandalous
   c. efforts not to use plastic
   d. it is our generation that will suffer from it
   e. I often go there
   f. the dump gave us bags
   g. the dump bought them back from us

1 *que* to introduce an opinion	2 direct object pronoun (DOP)	3 indirect object pronoun (IOP)	4 DOP and IOP used together	5 pronoun *en*	6 pronoun *y*	7 adverb after the verb	8 *pour* + negative infinitive

How do I watch out for words that have to be included in French?

French uses some words that we leave out in English. Make sure you include the connective *que* and determiners (such as articles) wherever they are needed.

1. Label each sentence **O** (opinion) or **R** (relative clause). If it helps, translate the sentences into English on paper.

   a. Je suis convaincu que le gouvernement va réduire les émissions de gaz. ☐

   b. La voiture que mon père a choisie est économique. ☐

   c. Les appareils qu'on achète consomment moins d'électricité. ☐

   d. Je pense qu'on peut générer moins de déchets. ☐

In English, the connective 'that' can be left out:

- in opinion phrases – 'I think (that) it is a scandal'
- in relative clauses – 'Cycling is the exercise (that) I prefer'.

The French equivalent, *que*, is always included:

- *Je pense* ***que*** *c'est un scandale.*
- *Le vélo, c'est l'exercice* ***que*** *je préfère.*

2. Translate these sentences into French. Each requires the connective *que*, even though the word 'that' is missing from the English – its position is flagged in the first three sentences to help you. Label each sentence **O** or **R**.

   a. I am certain ^ we can use less water. ☐ ....

   b. I'm sure ^ glass is recyclable. ☐ ....

   c. The bus ^ I take is electric. ☐ ....

   d. I know we should take a shower. ☐ ....

   e. I hope you've turned off the computer. ☐ ....

   f. The paper I use is recycled. ☐ ....

3. Add the missing determiner from the box to each 'good resolution' below. Label each sentence with the reason: **U** (uncountable noun), **Pl** (plural noun) and **+** or **–** (*plus/moins* phrases).

des	de	du	de l'	d'

French often uses determiners when English doesn't, especially with:

uncountable nouns (e.g. ***le*** *papier* – paper)

plural nouns (e.g. ***les*** *transports en commun* – public transport)

plus/moins (e.g. ***moins de*** *pollution* – less pollution).

Il faut …

   a. faire plus .... efforts pour protéger l'environnement. ☐

   b. acheter .... produits locaux. ☐

   c. boire rarement .... eau minérale. ☐

   d. consommer moins .... électricité. ☐

   e. préparer .... compost pour le jardin. ☐

   f. installer .... panneaux solaires. ☐

4. On paper, write three sentences of your own about what you do to help the environment. Include the connective *que* and articles with uncountable nouns or *plus/moins*.

2 How do I use correct verb forms?

In French, verb forms vary according to the **type of verb** (*-er, -ir* or *-re;* regular or irregular…), the **tense** and the **person**. Make sure you add the correct ending to the stem (the root) of the verb, and watch out for irregular verbs.

1. Read Érika's post. The verbs are underlined and the regular endings are in bold. For each verb, work out: the **type of verb**, the **tense** and the **person**. Copy them into the table.

*Au 20ème siècle, il y avait beaucoup d'orangs-outans à Sumatra. Dans 10 ans, il en rest**era** très peu. Récemment, je suis allée dans un zoo et j'en ai vu deux, que j'ai pris en photo. J'ét**ais** surprise parce qu'ils sont montés dans un arbre, puis le petit s'est caché dans sa cabane! Ils ét**aient** malheureux parce qu'ils préfèrer**aient** être en liberté. La survie des orangs-outans dépend de la forêt. Ils sont végétariens, se nourri**ssent** de fruits et ont donc besoin des arbres. Malheureusement, nous sommes égoïstes et nous détrui**sons** leur forêt!*

*Nous av**ions** un refuge pour animaux dans ma ville, mais il a fermé. J'espère que les propriétaires le rouvri**ront** un jour parce que nous pourrions alors soigner les animaux en danger.*

*Plus tard, je voudrais étudier les sciences de l'environnement. Si je chois**is** l'option «Animaux en danger», j'ir**ai** peut-être à Sumatra, ce qui me plair**ait** beaucoup! Je ne prends pas de décision maintenant, je vais y réfléchir. En attendant, les documentaires, c'est bien aussi. :-)*

Tense ↓ Person →			*je/j'*	*il/elle/on/c'*	*nous*	*ils/elles*
Present	regular	*-er*				
		-ir				
		-re				
	irregular					
Imperfect				*avait*		
Perfect	with *avoir*					
	with *être*					
Future						
Conditional						

2. **a** Find and highlight a perfect tense verb that agrees with:
   i a feminine singular subject **ii** a masculine plural subject.

   b Also highlight the subject of each of these verbs.

Remember that in the perfect tense with *être*, the past participle agrees with the subject.

3. Complete these sentences with the correct form of the verb in brackets. Decide on the correct tense for the context.

   a Si j'................................ [être] riche, je................................ [faire] le tour du monde.

   b L'été prochain, j'................................ [avoir] 18 ans et je .... [travailler] dans un refuge.

   c L'année dernière, une tempête .... [se produire] sur la côte et .... [détruire] les maisons.

   d Il y a 20 ans, la glace .... [fondre] et les ours polaires .... [partir].

   J'espère qu'ils .... [revenir] un jour!

3 How do I put object pronouns in the correct place and in the right order?

Direct object pronouns and the pronoun **en** are used to replace nouns (people or things). The pronoun **y** generally refers to a place. Indirect object pronouns stand for people, animals or organisations and are used with verbs that are normally followed by **à**. Always place object pronouns **in front of** the verb (which could be an infinitive).

1 **a** In the sentences below, highlight each direct object pronoun, underline the noun it stands for and circle the verb after the pronoun.

b Write **M** (masculine), **F** (feminine) or **Pl** (plural) in the box.

Example: Marina est une jeune SDF. Je la vois tous les jours dans la rue. F

la stands for Marina – Marina is the direct object.

i Les organisateurs d'Autremonde? Non, je ne les connais pas.

ii J'ai un voisin âgé mais je ne l'ai jamais rencontré.

iii Je n'ai rien dit à ma mère pour ne pas l'inquiéter.

2 In the sentences below, highlight each indirect object pronoun and underline the person it stands for (noun or subject pronoun). Circle the verb after the pronoun.

Example: Je connais une personne âgée isolée. Je lui rends souvent visite.

lui stands for *une personne*. It would be *rendre visite à une personne* so use the indirect object.

a Quand on m'a demandé d'aider les SDF, j'ai accepté.

b Nous avons écouté un conférencier qui nous a parlé de la pauvreté.

c Les chiens sont abandonnés et l'association va leur donner un refuge.

3 Add the missing object pronoun – direct, indirect, *en* or *y* – in the correct place in the second sentence of each pair. Underline the word(s) it replaces in the first sentence.

Example: Je connais un jeune SDF. Il *me* ^ parle de sa situation.

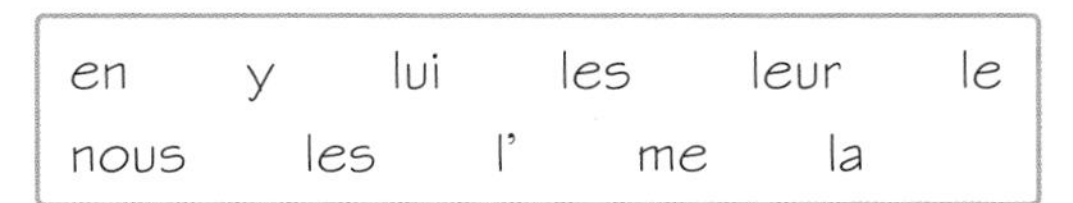

Use the grammar section in your textbook to revise object pronouns.

The pronoun *y* means 'there' or 'to there': *J'aide pendant le festival. J'**y** vais tous les ans.*
The pronoun *en* means 'of it/them' or 'some'. It refers to a noun or quantity already mentioned:
*La solitude des personnes âgées, il faut **en** prendre conscience.*
*Trois bénévoles? Non, il **en** faut beaucoup plus.*

a J'aide au refuge pour animaux. Je vais tous les samedis.

b La musique au festival est super. Les bénévoles aussi profitent.

c Je connais un vieux monsieur dans ma rue. Je vais téléphoner ce soir.

d Les sans-abri voudraient un logement et un travail. Comme je comprends!

In **e** and **f**, you need to use an indirect and a direct object pronoun together.
J'ai demandé le document et on me l'a donné.

e J'ai besoin de l'adresse de l'association. Ils vont envoyer.

f Au collège, nous avons demandé des informations sur le changement climatique. On a donné.

Sample response

Look at this exam-style writing task, similar to the one you saw on page 57.

Exam-style question

Faire du bénévolat

L'association «Mon frère, ma sœur» cherche des bénévoles pour travailler dans un restaurant pour les sans-abri. Écrivez un mail pour convaincre les organisateurs de vous offrir une place.

Vous **devez** faire référence aux points suivants:

- pourquoi vous voulez participer
- ce que vous avez déjà fait comme actions bénévoles
- les actions bénévoles que vous voulez faire plus tard
- pourquoi le bénévolat est important pour les jeunes.

Justifiez vos idées et vos opinions. Écrivez 130–150 mots environ **en français**. **(28 marks)**

Je suis convaincu que faire du bénévolat, c'est plus satisfaisant que jouer à des jeux vidéo! D'ailleurs, j'ai un peu d'expérience, puisqu'à Noël dernier, j'ai travaillé pour un Resto du cœur. D'abord, pour trouver des aliments, moi et les autres bénévoles sommes allés dans des supermarchés parce que les gens ont des provisions, et ils sont prêts à nous en donner. Ensuite, on m'a prêté un tablier et j'ai vidé et rempli le lave-vaisselle. Ce n'était pas très prestigieux, mais je ne l'ai pas regretté. Après le dîner, les bénévoles se sont assis avec les clients et nous les avons écoutés raconter leurs difficultés.*

Ça m'a ému et je suis sûr que j'y retournerai l'année prochaine mais j'aiderai peut-être à faire la cuisine. Je pense que le bénévolat est une bonne chose pour les jeunes. Ça nous donne le sentiment d'être utiles et en plus, ça nous permet d'élargir nos horizons. **Kamal**

* Resto du cœur – *soup kitchen*

1. In the student's answer, find and highlight the French translation for each of these phrases. Circle the French word in each phrase that does not have an equivalent in English.

   a playing video games
   b to find food
   c people have got shopping
   d after dinner
   e I'm sure I'll go back there
   f I think volunteering is a good thing

2. Find in the text and note down one example of each of these verb forms:

   a irregular verb, present, 1st person singular ....
   b irregular verb, perfect, 1st person plural ....
   c irregular verb, imperfect, 3rd person singular ....
   d reflexive verb, perfect, 3rd person plural ....
   e irregular verb, perfect, 3rd person singular ....
   f regular *-er* verb, future, 1st person singular ....

3. Find and underline the French equivalents of these phrases in the text. Circle the pronoun(s) in each French phrase. Note down the person or thing that each pronoun refers to.

   a they are ready to give us some
   b they lent me an apron
   c I didn't regret it
   d we listened to them
   e I will go back there
   f It lets us widen our horizons

Your turn!

You are now going to plan and write your response to the exam-style question from page 57.

Exam-style question

Notre environnement

Un magazine français cherche des articles sur l'environnement.

Écrivez au magazine pour expliquer pourquoi les problèmes d'environnement inquiètent les jeunes.

Vous **devez** faire référence aux points suivants:

1. Look back at the bullet points on page 57. First jot down your ideas in French.

   List two or three environmental problems you feel comfortable writing about.

   ....

   What matters most to young people? (e.g. Local or global environment? Problems getting worse?)

   ....

   What environmental action have you taken (e.g. picking up litter, recycling, encouraging others to turn lights off, etc.)? What action would you like to take in the future?

   ....

2. Write your answer to the exam-style question. Then check your work with the checklist.

   ....

Checklist In my answer do I …	✓
answer all the bullet points?	
express clear opinions and justify them?	
try my best to inform and interest the reader?	
use various time frames (past, present, future)?	
check for words that have to be included in French (connective *que*, articles)?	
check verb forms (the type of verb, the tense and the person)?	
check the position of object pronouns?	

Review your skills

Check up

Review your response to the exam-style question on page 63. Tick ✓ the column to show how well you think you have done each of the following.

	Not quite ✓	Nearly there ✓	Got it! ✓
watched out for words that have to be included in French, but not in English	☐	☐	☐
used correct verb forms	☐	☐	☐
put object pronouns in the correct place and the right order	☐	☐	☐

Need more practice?

On paper, plan and write your response to the exam-style question below.

Exam-style question

Notre festival

Votre ville voudrait attirer davantage de visiteurs étrangers à votre festival local.

Écrivez à un journal français pour expliquer ce qui est intéressant dans ce festival.

Vous **devez** faire référence aux points suivants:

- pourquoi ce festival est un succès
- les problèmes qui existaient dans ce festival
- comment on a résolu ces problèmes
- les projets d'avenir pour le festival.

Justifiez vos idées et vos opinions. Écrivez 130–150 mots environ **en français**. (28 marks)

To write a good answer, try to include:

- a clear message, even if some errors slip in
- a good standard of accuracy
- appropriate style and register
- individual opinions and justifications
- varied vocabulary and structures to interest, inform or convince
- creative use of language
- some complex sentences
- references to past, present and future events.

How confident do you feel about each of these **skills**? Colour in the bars.

1. How do I watch out for words that have to be included in French?
2. How do I use correct verb forms?
3. How do I put object pronouns in the correct place and in the right order?

Get started

9 Translating successfully into French

This unit will help you to be successful at translating from English into French. The skills you will build are to:

- make sure you include all key information
- produce a text that reads well in French
- avoid making errors.

In the exam, you will be asked to translate a paragraph from English into French. This unit will prepare you to look out for potential pitfalls and to translate the meaning of the English text into correct French.

Look at the exam-style question and sample student answer below.

Exam-style question

Une visite

Traduis le passage suivant **en français**:

I have been in France at my grandparents' since last Sunday. My little sister came with me and we travelled by plane. It was quick but she was scared! If it's hot, we will eat ice creams at the beach. When we are in Nice, I think we'll also visit cousins. I can't wait but it would be more fun if my parents were there. **(12 marks)**

Je suis en France chez mes grands-parents depuis dimanche dernier. Ma petite sœur est venue avec moi et on a voyagé en avion. C'était rapide mais elle avait peur! S'il fait chaud, nous mangerons des glaces à la plage. Quand nous serons à Nice, je pense que nous irons aussi voir des cousins. J'ai hâte mais ce serait plus amusant si mes parents étaient là.

The three key questions in the **skills boosts** will help you translate successfully into French.

1 How do I make sure I include all key information?

2 How do I produce a text that reads well in French?

3 How do I avoid making errors?

Get started

Look at Alicia's answer to the exam-style question below. She will not get full marks because she has made some mistakes. Read her translation and the hints in the callouts.

Exam-style question

L'avenir

Traduis le passage suivant **en français**:

I have been living in a small village since 2010. There is nothing to do here for teenagers. When I am at university, I will live in London. I can't wait! If I could I would study music as I am not bad in that subject but my parents think I should work in their shoe shop with them.

(12 marks)

1 what tense is needed with *depuis*?

3 what tense is needed after *quand* in the future?

5 check the tense is translated properly in a *si* sentence

7 check word order, as this affects meaning

J'ai habité dans un petit village depuis 2010. Il n'y a rien à faire ici pour ados.

Quand je suis à l'université, j'habiterai à Londres. Je ne peux pas attendre.

Si je pouvais, je voudrais étudier ... musique mais comme je suis mauvaise dans ce sujet, mes parents pensent ... je devrais travailler dans leur magasin de chaussures ....

2 use determiners in French even if absent in English

4 avoid word-for-word translation

6 include words that are absent in English but needed in French

8 check you don't miss negatives, as this will alter the meaning

9 beware of false friends

10 check the whole sentence is translated

① Use the hints to help you correct Alicia's translation. Write a correct translation here. The model answer on page 65 will help you find answers to the questions and suggestions in the callouts.

How do I make sure I include all key information?

A good translation must convey all the key information of the original text so make sure that:

- you take every word of the English text into account
- if you don't know how to say something in French, think creatively – don't leave it out!

Translation strategy 1

- Read the whole text before you start translating: this helps you to understand the context.
- Then break the text down into sections: this allows you to identify key messages so you can make sure you convey them all.

① Read this exam-style translation and separate the key points by inserting ✎ slashes. The first two have been done. How many key points are there altogether?

Exam-style question

Last Christmas, / my parents invited the whole family. / It was fun but also a bit tiring. I helped my mother to do the shopping and the cooking. I got lots of presents and my favourite was a mobile phone. Next Christmas, we will go skiing in France with friends. If I could, I would stay at home with my grandparents because I don't like winter sports at all!

Translation strategy 2

If you can't remember a word or phrase, try to use:

- a synonym
- a familiar phrase that will convey a similar meaning
- an approximation.

② Read Ben's attempt at translating the text above. He has missed three points and forgotten some words. Add ✎ the missing words and phrases to his text.

Noël dernier, mes parents ont invité toute la famille. C'était amusant mais aussi ^un peu fatigant. J'ai aidé ma mère à faire les courses. J'ai eu des cadeaux et mon préféré était un portable. Noël prochain, nous irons faire du ski en France. Si je pouvais, je resterais à la maison parce que je n'aime pas les sports d'hiver!

③ In this difficult text, Ben has highlighted several words/phrases he doesn't know. Find the correct translation (**A–G**) and a possible equivalent (**a–g**) and fill in ✎ the grid below.

Exam-style question

I don't like sport but as my parents are (1) health freaks, I have to (2) do bodybuilding. Last year, I went to a holiday camp for a (3) fortnight and we swam every morning in the river. It was (4) a nightmare! (5) Nonetheless I was (6) delighted because it was there that I met my new girlfriend Alice. Next year, Alice and I will go to France and (7) sunbathe on the beach.

A un cauchemar	**E** néanmoins	**a** mais	**e** faire des exercices physiques
B fanas de santé	**F** deux semaines	**b** très content	**f** un certain temps
C ravi	**G** faire de la musculation	**c** rester au soleil	**g** très intéressés par la santé
D se faire bronzer		**d** horrible	

1			2			3			4			5			6			7		
1	*B*	*g*	2			3			4			5			6			7		

2 How do I produce a text that reads well in French?

You need to find the balance between taking every English word into account and producing a text which is correct and reads well in French. Pay special attention to:

- words that are absent in English but needed in French (see Unit 8, page 59)
- word order
- set French expressions and structures.

1 Read sentences a–j. Correct the 'gibberish' French translations below each sentence. The number of changes needed is indicated in brackets.

a My parents think I should go to university.
Mes parents pensent je devrais aller à université. (2)

b The pastime I prefer is football.
Le passe-temps je préfère, c'est football. (2)

c I like watching films but I have never liked comedies.
J'aime regarder films mais je n'ai jamais aimé comédies. (2)

d He always buys a card for her sister's birthday ...
Il toujours achète une carte pour sa sœur anniversaire ... (3)

e ... but he never gives it to her.
... mais il ne jamais donne la à elle. (3)

f We only like French music.
Nous seulement aimons française musique. (3)

g I walk to school on Mondays.
Je marche à l'école sur lundis. (3)

h Now and again I like going for a walk.
Maintenant et encore, j'aime aller pour une marche. (2)

i What I like doing in the evening is reading.
Quoi j'aime faire dans le soir, c'est lire. (2)

j My brother has just arrived in Scotland.
Mon frère est juste arrivé en Écosse. (3)

Translation strategy 3
English → 'gibberish' → French
Translate each sentence word for word in your head, then correct this 'gibberish' with equivalent French vocabulary and structures, using the grammatical rules you have learned.

In sentences a–c, look out for absent words in English.

In sentences d–f, look out for word order.

In sentences g–j, look out for set expressions and structures.

2 Keeping this strategy in mind, translate this text on paper.
Pay particular attention to the underlined words and phrases and the gaps.

Exam-style question

My father retired last month. He used to work in a bank but he never liked his job. Now he hopes ... he'll be able to do what he likes best: he loves ... yoga and ... gardening. I have just promised him ... I will often help him in the garden. I like planting ... vegetables even if I can't stand eating them!

3 How do I avoid making errors?

To get the highest mark possible, your translation needs to be as faultless as possible. This means you need to check your text carefully to avoid mistakes that will hinder clarity.

Translation strategy 4
Keep a mental checklist for accuracy:
- correct choice of words
- correct use of pronouns
- correct verbs and tense formation.

1 Complete each translation by circling (A) the correct option. Make sure the word you choose makes sense in the context and is not a false friend.

a I spent my holiday in France. J'ai **dépensé / passé** mes vacances en France.

b The heating wasn't working. Le chauffage ne **marchait / travaillait** pas.

c The journey back was tiresome. **La journée / Le voyage** retour était pénible.

d I couldn't rest at all. Je n'ai pas pu **rester / me reposer** du tout.

2 Make sure you know how to form verbs in French. Translate the following into French:

a I am working ....

b I was working ....

c I would work ....

d I used to work ....

e I will work ....

f I have been working ....

False friends: the word you choose must make sense.
I had an **injury** on one **arm**: *j'ai eu une* ***blessure*** (not *une injure* = insult) *sur un* ***bras*** (not *une arme* = weapon)

French verbs are usually made up of only one or two words.
French one-word tenses: present, imperfect, future, conditional
French two-word tenses: perfect, pluperfect (auxiliary + past participle), near future (*aller* + infinitive)

3 Complete these translations.

a **Playing** tennis is fun. .... au tennis, c'est amusant.

b By **playing** tennis, you keep fit. .... au tennis, on garde la forme.

c I am **playing** tennis tomorrow. .... au tennis demain.

d I like **playing** tennis with Hugo. .... au tennis avec Hugo.

e Before **playing** tennis, I did judo. .... au tennis, je faisais du judo.

f After **playing** tennis, I had lunch. .... au tennis, j'ai déjeuné.

g I want **to** play this game. Je veux .... jouer à ce jeu.

h You need time **to** play this game. Il faut du temps .... jouer à ce jeu.

i It's possible **to** go to France. C'est possible .... aller en France.

j He encourages me **to** go to France. Il m'encourage .... aller en France.

k My friend wants me **to** go with him. Mon copain veut que .... avec lui.

There is more than one way to translate a verb ending in '-ing' or with 'to' in front of it so be careful when completing these translations.

Sample response

Look at this exam-style question and the sample answer below.

Exam-style question

Mon temps libre

Traduis le passage suivant **en français**:

I have been a volunteer for three months. By working in the retirement home, I help to entertain the elderly people. I love it! I often play the piano and I sing as well but the residents only like old-fashioned songs! My parents encourage me to have a small job to earn money. I would do that if I had time. **(12 marks)**

This translation contains many mistakes. The callouts point out some of them. Read them to remind yourself of the work you have done in this unit. Try to spot the other mistakes too, such as false friends, adjectival agreement, how to translate 'to' and missing determiners. The gaps (...) mark where a word is missing.

J'ai été volontaire pour trois mois.
Par aller dans la maison de retirement, j'aide pour divertir les vieux gens.
... ...
Je souvent joue le piano et je chante bien mais les résidents aiment ... ... chansons démodé!
Mes parents encourage moi ... avoir un petit boulot de gagner de la monnaie.
Je voudrais faire ça si j'avais ... temps.

Use *depuis* with the present tense. If you can't remember the word for 'volunteer' think of a synonym.

Remember the different ways to translate a verb ending in *–ing*. Try to remember set French expressions (e.g for 'elderly people').

Check you don't miss out any part of the text!

Check word order (adverb). Check words are not missed out (especially when they affect meaning, e.g. 'as well').

Check verb endings. What object pronoun is needed here and in what position?

What verb form is needed to translate 'I would' + verb? Check if a determiner is needed before *temps*.

1 Write a corrected translation below.

....

....

....

....

....

....

Your turn!

You are now going to write your response to this exam-style question. (This practice text is longer than the one you will encounter in the exam.) Read the English text and check out the tips in the callouts.

Exam-style question

Traduis le passage suivant **en français**:

I bought a new mobile to replace the old one (1) I lost because I need a phone for (1) homework. I am (2) not keen on it. If I (3) could, I (3) would buy an iPhone but my parents think (1) it's (2) far too expensive. We have (1) computers at home as my mother uses (4) them for (1) work: she is a (5) novelist. When I (3) go to uni, I (3) will study (1) literature. My parents (4) really hope (1) I (3) will be able to become a (6) librarian. **(12 marks)**

1 Which word that is absent in English do you need to include in French?

2 Remember: you can't always translate word for word!

3 Which tense and verb form do you need?

4 Word order can be different, e.g. adjectives, pronouns and adverbs

5 Stuck on a word? How will you get around it?

6 Beware of this false friend!

① Write your answer to the exam-style question. Then check your work with the checklist.

French nouns nearly always need a determiner, unlike English nouns:

I love fish	*J'aime **le** poisson*
I eat fish	*Je mange **du** poisson*
I don't eat fish	*Je ne mange pas **de** poisson.*

One notable exception is professions:
My mother is a dentist. *Ma mère est dentiste.*
unless it is qualified by an adjective:
My mum is a good dentist. Ma mère est *une bonne* dentiste.

Checklist In my answer do I ...	✓
include all key information?	
take every word into account?	
use a synonym if necessary?	
include any extra words needed in French?	
pay attention to French word order?	
avoid translating word for word?	
avoid false friends?	
use pronouns correctly?	
use correct verb formation?	

Review your skills

Check up

Review your response to the exam-style question on page 71. Tick the column to show how well you think you have done each of the following.

	Not quite	Nearly there	Got it!
made sure I included all key information	☐	☐	☐
produced a text that reads well in French	☐	☐	☐
avoided making errors	☐	☐	☐

Need more practice?

On paper, write your responses to the exam-style questions below.

A

Exam-style question

Une fête

Traduis le passage suivant **en français**:

When I was younger I used to celebrate Christmas with my grandparents. We ate turkey and vegetables and my dad always made a chocolate log. Last year, my parents decided to spend the Christmas holiday in France so we all went to Paris. I thought it was a great idea but next Christmas, I plan to work in a shop to earn money which I must have to pay for my studies. I will go to uni if I pass my exams. **(12 marks)**

B

Exam-style question

Chez moi

Traduis le passage suivant **en français**:

I have just arrived in London. Before coming here, I lived in the countryside. I was fond of our old house which was small and cosy and had a huge garden. Now we live in a flat which my parents bought recently. I have to share a bedroom with my brother, which I hate! I would really prefer to have my own space. When I have children, they will have a bedroom each! **(12 marks)**

To write a good translation you need to:
- show that you have understood all points
- communicate all those points clearly
- use accurate vocabulary and structures
- write a text which reads like a French text, not a word-for-word translation of the original
- use French word order in sentences
- be as error-free as possible: remember to check spellings, accents, adjectival agreements
- use correct tense and verb endings.

How confident do you feel about each of these **skills**? Colour in the bars.

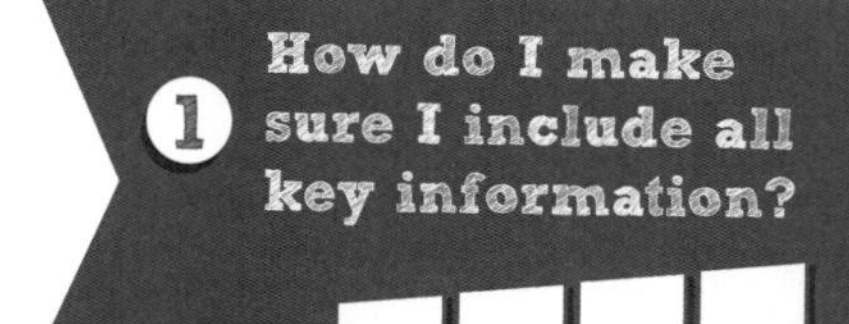

1 How do I make sure I include all key information?

2 How do I produce a text that reads well in French?

3 How do I avoid making errors?

Answers

Unit 1

Page 2

1 Circled and numbered 1–4 as colour-coded here:

1 2 3 4

Je m'entends bien avec mon frère, Thomas. On se chamaille quelquefois mais par contre, si j'ai des problèmes, je peux me confier à lui. Au collège, ma meilleure copine s'appelle Chloé. Elle est intelligente mais pas prétentieuse. En plus, elle est très généreuse et en particulier, elle m'aide quand on fait nos devoirs. Chloé et moi, on s'est connues à l'école primaire. En fait, elle était timide quand elle était petite. Ensuite, on a commencé le collège ensemble et on est restées amies. D'ailleurs, ce week-end, je vais retrouver Chloé en ville et on va voir un feu d'artifice.

2
- les personnes que tu aimes bien – **present**
- les qualités personnelles de ces personnes – **present**
- ton/ta meilleur(e) ami(e) à l'école primaire – **past: imperfect and/or perfect**
- les personnes que tu vas voir ce week-end – **future**

3
a mais par contre, (expresses a contrast)
b en plus,
c en particulier,
d en fait,
e d'ailleurs,

Page 3

1
a The highlighting below shows the content that links to the first two bullet points.
b The last two bullet points should be circled.
- Jack says he met his best friend Dylan at judo club, but he doesn't mention his best friend at primary school.
- He says he often goes to the skatepark at the weekend, but he doesn't mention who he is going to see this weekend.

c Irrelevant information crossed out below.

J'aime bien mon beau-père, Simon, parce qu'il a le sens de l'humour. On va au foot ensemble et même quand notre équipe perd, il est cool et il voit le bon côté des choses. ~~Par contre, je ne m'entends pas du tout avec ma belle-mère, qui est toujours pessimiste.~~ Mon meilleur copain s'appelle Dylan. On s'est rencontrés parce qu'on faisait du judo ensemble et maintenant on est dans la même classe au collège. Dylan est toujours de bonne humeur et il me fait rire. On va souvent au skatepark le week-end.
• les personnes que tu aimes bien • les qualités personnelles de ces personnes • ton/ta meilleur(e) ami(e) à l'école primaire • les personnes que tu vas voir ce week-end.

2 a–b
A f, Pa (perfect)
B d, Pa (perfect and imperfect)
C b, F
D c, F
E a, Pr
F e, Pa (imperfect)

Page 4

1
a
A Besides/As it happens, I bought the CD.
B To be frank, we were happy but very tired.
C The acrobats in particular were fantastic.
D Moreover, there was a good atmosphere.
E In fact/As a matter of fact, it's the best time to visit the town.

b 1 E 2 C 3 A 4 D 5 B

2
a Cependant,
b Malheureusement,
c D'un autre côté,
d D'ailleurs,
e En revanche,
f Franchement,

3 Sample answers:
a Ma copine Lucie est très généreuse. Malheureusement, elle travaille trop et elle n'est pas souvent libre.
b Je m'entends bien avec Paul. D'ailleurs, on passe tous les week-ends ensemble.
c Je n'aime pas la nouvelle pizzéria. En plus, les pizzas sont chères.
d Ma sortie préférée le samedi soir, c'est aller au bowling. En revanche, je ne joue pas bien.

Page 5

1
a Nous **marchions** au bord de la mer quand nous **avons vu** un sous-marin jaune.
b Hier, il **est resté** au lit parce qu'il **était** malade.

2 Sample answer:
Quand j'étais petit(e), j'aimais le fromage et j'adorais le chocolat.

3
a C – Il fait de la natation le lundi.
b A – Mes grands-parents adorent lire/la lecture.
c E – Il courait quand il est tombé.
d B – Elle porte un pull bleu.
e D – Ils/Elles font leurs devoirs.

4
a Je pense que mon ami(e) doit être plus gentil(le).
b Mon ami/amie dit que nous devons/qu'on doit partir en vacances ensemble.

Page 6

ce qu'on peut faire le soir	café Chez Fred nouveau cinéma du centre commercial concert de rock
les aspects positifs	Chez Fred: jouer au baby-foot, boissons pas chères concert: une soirée exceptionnelle
les aspects négatifs	nouveau cinéma: loin, il faut prendre le bus concert: elle ne doit pas sortir tard
ta dernière sortie	anniversaire: film au nouveau cinéma
ce que tu vas faire ce week-end	concert de rock

2 parce qu', En plus, Malheureusement, mais d'un autre côté

3 a **c'était** mon anniversaire et **j'ai vu** un film
- b il faut prendre (le bus)
- c je vais aller (à un concert de rock)
- d Mon père dit que je ne dois pas sortir tard le soir

Page 8

Sample answer:

J'admire énormément mon grand-père. Je pense que c'est un homme très courageux. Quand il était petit, il est tombé très malade et malheureusement il est devenu handicapé. Cependant, il est retourné à l'école, il a beaucoup travaillé, en particulier en maths, et il est allé à l'université. Franchement, je trouve que c'est impressionnant. Moi, par contre, je ne suis pas bonne en maths, mais je vais étudier le chinois et ensuite je vais voyager en Chine. Mes parents disent que je ne dois pas partir si loin, mais je veux être aussi courageuse que mon grand-père.

Unit 2

Page 10

1 a *Blade Runner*
- b science fiction
- c big screen and comfortable seats; less convenient and more expensive than Netflix
- d He'll go to the cinema with friends to see the latest James Bond movie.

2 a bons, grand, dernier*
- b circle the following: dernier*, novateur, atmosphérique, passionnant, intéressant, spéciaux, confortables, pratique, chère, prochain

  * *dernier* changes meaning according to its position: to mean 'last' as in 'last month' or 'last Monday', place it after the noun; to mean 'the latest', place it before the noun.
- c assez, très, vraiment
- d underline the following: généralement, souvent
- e superlative: le plus (intéressant), comparatives: plus (pratique), moins (chère)
- f highlight the following: comme, par exemple

Page 11

1 a relaxante
- b passionnant, ennuyeux
- c parfait, fatigantes
- d originales, excellents

2 a J'ai une **grosse** chienne **noire**. Le dimanche, je mets un **vieux** survêtement **confortable** et je la sors à la campagne.
- b J'adore cette bande dessinée pour ses **nombreux** personnages **amusants** et ses **belles** illustrations **originales**.
- c Mon passe-temps préféré, c'est faire de **bons** gâteaux **appétissants** avec de **jolies** décorations **colorées**.

3 a J'aime le sport. Pour moi, le football est moins exigeant que le rugby. Je pense que le sport le moins exigeant, c'est le golf.
- b J'aime (regarder) la télé. Pour moi, les documentaires sont plus informatifs que les jeux télévisés. Je pense que le documentaire le plus informatif, c'est *Blue Planet*.
- c J'aime le cinéma. Pour moi, les films romantiques sont moins ennuyeux que les films de science-fiction. Je pense que le film le moins ennuyeux, c'est *Love Actually*.

Page 12

1 –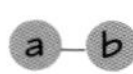

When	How	How often	To what degree
maintenant	*probablement*	*parfois*	*tellement*
hier	bien	toujours	assez
récemment	gentiment	souvent	vraiment
demain	mal	rarement	beaucoup
Additional words might include:			
aujourd'hui tôt tard enfin actuellement bientôt ensuite après-demain avant-hier	sans doute vite *most adverbs ending in –ment:* rapidement calmement lentement *etc.*	parfois de temps en temps jamais régulièrement tout le temps occasionnellement tous les jours	très peu trop relativement

2 a Je ~~vraiment~~ suis **vraiment** passionnée de lecture.
- b Je ~~toujours~~ télécharge **toujours** des livres sur ma liseuse.
- c Je ~~rarement~~ lis **rarement** des bandes dessinées.
- d Ma mère est **tellement** contente ~~tellement~~ quand je lis!
- e Mon père pense que je ne suis pas **assez** active ~~assez~~.
- f Je ne fais **probablement** pas ~~probablement~~ assez de sport.
- g Je ~~parfois~~ vais **parfois** à la piscine mais pas ~~souvent~~ assez **souvent**.
- h Je ~~souvent~~ lis **souvent** le soir avant de dormir.

③ Sample answer:

Je vais **assez souvent** au cinéma de l'Institut français parce que les films français m'intéressent **beaucoup/vraiment**.

Hier, j'ai vu un film avec Gad Elmaleh, un acteur que j'aime **bien/beaucoup**. Je trouve qu'il joue **toujours vraiment** bien! Ma sœur, qui n'aime pas le cinéma, est **gentiment** venue avec moi, alors **demain**, en échange, je vais aller au match de foot avec elle!

Page 13

① a mais/par contre b sauf
c surtout d comme/par exemple

② A c B d C a D b

③ Sample answers:

a Je vais souvent à des concerts; en effet, c'est un de mes passe-temps préférés.

b Le week-end dernier, je suis allé à un concert de Mozart et c'était fantastique.

c J'écoute souvent la radio, surtout le soir, quand je rentre de l'école, parce que ça me relaxe.

d Comme je joue bien du violon, l'année prochaine, je vais jouer dans l'orchestre de l'école.

e J'aime bien jouer du violon mais par contre, je n'aime pas pratiquer tous les jours!

Page 14

①

Which answer ...	A	B	How is this done?
answers the question fully?	✓	✓	by addressing all four bullet points
gives relevant facts only?		✓	A says: *C'est un grand sportif et il aime bien jouer au tennis avec moi* = not relevant
uses interesting adjectives?		✓	A uses *excentrique* but otherwise sticks to common adjectives (*intéressante, super*) B uses: *meilleure, accueillant, inoubliable*
uses correct adjective agreement?	✓	✓	no errors on agreement
positions adjectives correctly?	✓	✓	no errors on position
uses a comparative or a superlative?		✓	*le plus souvent; ma meilleure copine; le plus accueillant;*
uses adverbs appropriately?	✓	✓	A: *normalement, généralement, beaucoup* B: *le plus souvent, très, beaucoup, régulièrement, vraiment, bien, d'abord, ensuite, probablement*
expands on key points?		✓	A: *par exemple Décathlon* B: *parce qu'on s'entend très bien mais j'aime aussi beaucoup sortir avec ma famille; Par exemple, hier, nous sommes allées à Starbuck*
uses connectives to explain/illustrate?		✓	A: *par exemple* B: *parce que, mais, par exemple, comme*
uses past and/or future tenses?	✓	✓	A: *je sors, nous allons, je suis allé, nous avons vu, je ferai, nous irons manger* B: *je sors, allons, sommes allées, j'ai visité, nous nous sommes amusés, c'était, je finirai, j'irai*

② Sample answer:

Je sors le plus souvent avec ma famille et de temps en temps avec des copains.

En ville, je vais généralement dans les grands magasins, comme Selfridges, mais avec mes copains, on va au centre sportif. En effet, il a une piscine formidable.

Pendant ma dernière sortie, je suis allé voir une nouvelle exposition fascinante et gratuite sur les premiers jeux vidéo, comme par exemple Space Invaders.

J'aimerais vraiment y retourner avec mon frère le week-end prochain si c'est possible. Après on ira voir un nouveau film d'action au cinéma.

Page 16

Sample answer:

Pour moi, Facebook est le réseau social le plus approprié puisque tous mes amis y sont et on peut communiquer très facilement.

Les avantages des réseaux sociaux sont, par exemple, de pouvoir communiquer avec ses amis et voir leurs photos. Par contre, il faut faire attention à bien protéger son identité.

Hier, j'ai partagé les photos de mon week-end à Paris et mes amis ont fait des commentaires hilarants qui m'ont beaucoup amusé(e)! Ce soir, je vais poster un beau poème romantique et émouvant et j'espère que mes amis l'aimeront aussi.

Unit 3

Page 18

① a le petit déjeuner – breakfast

b le brunch – brunch

c le goûter – afternoon snack/tea

d le repas de Noël – Christmas lunch

② a un petit déjeuner **copieux**

b c'est **essentiel**

c un moment **convivial**

d **inoubliable**

e **savoureux**

3 i Sample answers:
- a je pense vraiment que
- b commencer la journée
- c parler
- d je mangeais beaucoup de
- e j'aime

ii Answers from the text:
- je suis convaincu que
- démarrer la journée
- bavarder
- je dévorais des
- j'apprécie

4
- où et quand vous mangez habituellement – present tense
- ce qui est important pour vous dans les repas – present tense
- un repas mémorable – perfect and imperfect tenses
- vos repas quand vous serez adulte – future tense

Page 19

1
- a J'aime les desserts, mais **j'apprécie** aussi les plats salés.
- b À Noël, **je me régale avec** la bûche au chocolat. Miam!
- c **J'aime bien** les légumes, mais je ne suis pas fan.
- d Mardi gras, c'est ma fête préférée parce que **j'adore** le carnaval!
- e Coller un poisson dans le dos des gens le 1er avril, **ça m'amuse**.
- f Aller danser le soir du 14 juillet, **ça me plaît**.

2 A d B b C a D c

3 Mon copain voudrait aller au carnaval parce qu'il **adore** les chars fleuris. Moi aussi, j'**aime bien** les chars, mais je ne suis pas fan. J'ai **expliqué** qu'il y a trop de monde au carnaval et j'ai **ajouté** que tout est cher dans les cafés. Il a **précisé** qu'il ne veut pas aller au carnaval le samedi mais le vendredi, parce qu'il y a moins de monde. J'ai accepté, parce que même si je ne suis pas fan des chars, j'**apprécie** la musique. En plus, les sucreries, **ça me plaît** et je vais **me régaler** avec les gaufres au Nutella!

Page 20

1 a–b

Quand mon père et sa compagne Cécile se sont mariés, ils ont organisé une ~~belle~~ fête **conviviale**. Pour commencer, un vendeur de glaces est venu sur son tricycle! C'était ~~bien~~ **original** et les glaces étaient ~~bonnes~~ **délicieuses**. Il y avait un ~~très bon~~ orchestre de jazz **divertissant**. On a aussi organisé un lâcher de ballons. C'était ~~beau~~ **émouvant** et Cécile a un peu pleuré. Pendant le dîner, le père de Cécile a raconté **des** ~~mauvaises~~ blagues **ridicules**, mais tout le monde souriait. La seule chose ~~négative~~ **décevante**, c'était le temps, parce qu'il a plu toute la journée. En plus, les enfants couraient partout, c'était ~~nul~~ **agaçant**. Après le dîner, on a servi un ~~très gros et très beau~~ **superbe** gâteau. Au final, c'était une ~~très bonne~~ fête **réussie**. Quels ~~bons~~ souvenirs **inoubliables**!

2 Sample answers:
- a Pour l'anniversaire de mon grand-père, on a fait une petite fête très conviviale. Ma grand-mère avait préparé un gâteau délicieux et l'ambiance était émouvante.
- b Pour le réveillon de Noël, on est allés chez ma tante. On a chanté des chants traditionnels, c'était divertissant. En plus, le dîner était très réussi. C'était une soirée inoubliable.
- c Pour son mariage, ma cousine Sophie portait une robe originale, mais superbe. Par contre, la musique disco était un peu ridicule.

Page 21

1
- a D – pour garder la forme
- b C – ça vaut la peine
- c G – j'ai mangé comme quatre
- d D – j'avais les yeux plus gros que le ventre
- e B – ça me manque
- f F – je donne un coup de main
- g E – ça me tient à cœur

2
- a **Ça vaut la peine** d'aller au carnaval de la Guadeloupe, même si c'est loin.
- b Quand mes parents sont absents, les repas en famille, **ça me manque**.
- c Aller au mariage de mon frère, **ça me tient à cœur** parce que je vais être témoin.
- d Le samedi, **je donne un coup de main** à mon père pour faire le ménage.

3 In the French sentences, there is an extra **comma** and an extra word (**ce** or **ça**).

4
- a Ma glace préférée**, c'est** le sorbet au citron.
- b Le concert**, ça** m'a beaucoup plu.
- c J'essaie de manger équilibré, mais le chocolat**, ça** me manque.

Page 22

1
- a suis convaincue
- b apprécient
- c renseigné
- d que nous accueillerons

2 entertaining – *distrayante/divertissants*; life-enhancing – *enrichissante*; varied – *variés*; lively – *entraînante*; touching – *touchante*; moving – *pleine d'émotion*; unforgettable – *inoubliable*

3 Highlighted phrases in the text:
- a Folkfest, c'est un festival de danse folk.
- b Folkfest, c'est un festival qui me tient à cœur
- c Cette soirée, c'était une expérience inoubliable.

Page 24

Sample answer (with interesting verbs, adjectives and idioms highlighted):

J'apprécie vraiment les fêtes de famille si les cousins de mon âge viennent aussi. On parle des vacances qu'on passait ensemble chez nos grands-parents quand on était petits et on rit comme des fous. Par contre, les rencontres avec seulement mes oncles et tantes âgés, je trouve ça déprimant.

Récemment, j'ai assisté au baptême de Miriam, le bébé de mon cousin Harry. C'était une journée conviviale parce que tous mes cousins se sont déplacés. Après l'église, nous avons déjeuné dans un restaurant simple mais réputé. Ce repas, c'était un vrai festin et j'ai mangé comme quatre! On a pris des photos sans arrêt et on va les mettre en ligne.

La prochaine fête de famille, ce sera le mariage de ma grande sœur l'année prochaine. C'est une occasion qui me tient à cœur parce que je suis très proche de ma sœur. Je suis convaincue que ça va être mémorable et émouvant.

Unit 4

Page 26

1 a It's a pleasant town (*agréable*); it's by the sea (*au bord de la mer*); there's a micro-climate (*un microclimat*)

b the town has built a sports centre (*la commune a construit un centre sportif*) – many families had contacted the mayor and told him the children were bored (*beaucoup de familles avaient contacté le maire et lui avaient dit que les enfants s'ennuyaient*)

c the mayor intends to open a youth club next year (*une maison des jeunes l'an prochain*)

d a multiplex cinema (*j'aimerais avoir un cinéma multi-salles*)

2 Pluperfect: avaient contacté, avaient dit

Imperfect: étais, avait, était, s'ennuyaient, était

Perfect: s'est améliorée, a construit, a aménagé

Present: vis, habitons, adore, est, a, fait, aiment, est

Near future/future: ouvrira, pourra, va s'amuser, sera

Conditional: aimerais, serait

3 a Highlighted phrases: **i** Ma famille et moi; **ii** les gens

b Underlined phrases: a aussi l'intention d'ouvrir; Quand elle ouvrira; on pourra; On va bien s'amuser, j'aimerais avoir; Plouester serait

Page 27

1 a Samedi après-midi, mes amis et moi sommes allés au cinéma.

b Personne n'a aimé le film.

c Dimanche, mes parents m'ont invitée au restaurant.

d Ma sœur m'a donné un super cadeau.

e On a beaucoup ri et on s'est bien amusés.

f Et toi, qu'est-ce que tu as fait ce week-end en ville?

g En général, ça me plaît beaucoup d'aller en ville le week-end.

2 Sample answer:

Ma mère, ma sœur et moi habitons à Vannes. Nous avons/On a un assez petit appartement au centre-ville/ Notre appartement, situé au centre-ville, est assez petit. À mon avis/Selon moi/Pour moi, les gens sont accueillants ici. Comme moi, les visiteurs apprécient la beauté de la ville.

Ma sœur et moi allons souvent à la plage/Ma sœur vient souvent à la plage avec moi.

Elle aime/On aime/Nous aimons/Ma sœur et moi aimons aller faire du shopping ensemble dans la zone piétonne.

Page 28

1 a était parti b avais pris c avait acheté

d avions visité e avions réservé f avait vu

A d B b C a D e E f F c

2 Sample answers:

a qu'on nous avait recommandé/que nous n'avions pas encore goûté. C'était très bon.

b nous n'avions pas (bien) dormi/le voyage avait été fatigant. Nous n'étions pas contents.

c elle avait perdu son passeport/elle s'était blessée au pied. C'était triste.

3 a Le train vient *(juste/à peine)* de partir, vous arrivez/ tu arrives trop tard!

b Je viens *(juste/à peine)* d'acheter mon billet de train.

c Le train venait *(juste/à peine)* de partir quand je suis arrivé(e) à la gare.

d Nous venions *(juste/à peine)* de finir notre visite quand le parc a fermé.

Page 29

1 a **Words/phrases which indicate the future:**

quand + future tense, je veux + infinitive, s'il fait beau, j'ai envie de + infinitive, j'aimerais + infinitive, j'ai l'intention de + infinitive, j'espère que, si c'est possible, j'ai décidé de + infinitive, je rêve de + infinitive

b **Verbs in the near future:**

on va faire, tu vas t'amuser

c **Verbs in the future tense:**

tu viendras, on visitera, on ira, on aura

d **Verbs in the conditional:**

j'aimerais + infinitive, je voudrais + infinitive, j'habiterais

2 a Quand mon ami(e) viendra, on ira au marché.

b Si on a le temps, on visitera le château.

c Si c'était moins loin, on irait à la plage.

d J'espère que nous pourrons aller nous promener au bord de la mer.

e Je rêve de faire des randonnées à la campagne.

f J'ai l'intention de montrer la vieille ville à mon ami(e).

g J'ai décidé de faire une promenade en bateau.

Page 30

1

subjects other than *je*	les paysages on, il, *ce/c'*, nous, des amis, ma mère, tu
verbs in the present tense	adore, sont, mange, aime, est, a, viens, espère, viens
verbs in the perfect tense	a visité, a attendu, nous sommes promenés,
verbs in the imperfect tense	étions, avait, était, faisait, pouvait
verbs in the pluperfect tense	avaient recommandé, avait réservé
a phrase about the very recent past	je viens de passer
verbs in the near future	va retourner
verbs in the future tense	pourras, fera
verbs in the conditional	irais, aimerais
phrases which indicate the future	j'espère que tu pourras, j'aimerais te montrer, Si tu viens, on fera

Page 32

Sample answer:

Notre ville, Loumont, est très agréable mais il n'y a rien à faire pour les jeunes et il n'y a aucun local pour se retrouver. Beaucoup de jeunes s'ennuient et font des bêtises. Ensuite, ils ont des problèmes avec la police. Il est urgent de faire quelque chose.

Un groupe de jeunes a proposé de créer un foyer pour les jeunes. Ils espèrent utiliser la salle de sport, qui est fermée le soir. Ils aimeraient payer des animateurs pour faire des ateliers de théâtre ou de musique. Le maire, à qui ils avaient déjà parlé plusieurs fois, a dit qu'il n'y avait pas assez d'argent.

Alors, des jeunes ont décidé de collecter de l'argent. Avec cet argent, nous allons pouvoir payer des animateurs. On ne s'ennuiera plus en ville!

Personnellement, comme je fais partie d'un groupe de musique, j'ai organisé des concerts dans les rues de la ville. Nous avons gagné beaucoup d'argent!

Unit 5

Page 34

1. b, c, d

2.

1	un pays	7	Kaycee
2	la Tunisie	8	les bracelets
3	la Tunisie	9	la vendeuse
4	Tunis	10	Kaycee
5	les bracelets	11	la Tunisie
6	les bracelets	12	la Tunisie

3.
- a vient de
- b Après avoir
- c En lisant
- d visiterais
- e je sois
- f en train de

Page 35

1. A a B c C d D b

2.
- a qui ne contient pas de viande.
- b qu'ils connaissent bien.

3.
- a Ce que j'ai apprécié, c'est la cuisine locale.
- b Ce qui me dégoûte, c'est la soupe à l'oignon.

4. Sample answers:
- a Pendant que je faisais du shopping au marché, mes parents écrivaient des cartes postales.
- b Au moment où nous sommes arrivés à la gare, le taxi est tombé en panne.
- c Quand je suis allé au marché de Noël, j'ai mangé des gaufres au sucre./ Pendant que j'étais au marché de Noël, j'ai mangé des gaufres au sucre.
- d Au moment où je suis rentré dans le café, mon téléphone a sonné.

Page 36

1. Mon week-end à la montagne avec Sunita a mal commencé! Pourtant, on le préparait depuis longtemps et on l'attendait avec impatience. Mon père m'a déposée à la gare à 8 heures. J'avais rendez-vous avec Sunita mais je ne la voyais pas. Je l'ai appelée, mais pas de réponse. À 8h20, Sunita est arrivée ... avec mes chaussures de marche à la main! Je les avais oubliées chez elle. Je l'ai embrassée. Le chef de gare nous a aidées à monter dans le train et on l'a remercié.

2.
- a Je l'ai acheté.
- b Elle la retrouve.
- c Il les regarde.
- d Elle le conduit à l'aéroport.
- e «Je suis en retard, Maman! Tu **me** déposes à la gare?»
- f «Notre avion atterrit à midi. Tu viens **nous** chercher?»

3. À mon grand-père? Oui, je lui ai écrit.

À mes cousins? Oui, je leur ai écrit.

Aux voisins? Oui, je leur ai écrit.

À mon oncle et ma tante? Oui, je leur ai écrit.

À ma sœur? Oui, je lui ai écrit.

4.
- a On a passé une nuit au camping. On **y** a passé une nuit.
- b Elle a mangé beaucoup de pâtisseries. Elle **en** a mangé beaucoup.
- c Nous allons assister au concert. Nous allons **y** assister.
- d J'ai aperçu des dauphins. J'**en** ai aperçu.
- e Ils sont allés à Paris. Ils **y** sont allés.
- f J'ai vu deux singes. J'**en** ai vu deux.

Page 37

1. Nous venons d'arriver à Essaouira. Après être allés à l'hôtel et après avoir mangé, nous explorons maintenant la vieille ville. Je t'écris en mangeant une glace dans un café du souk. J'adore le souk, bien que ce soit très bruyant!

Mes parents sont en train de discuter le prix d'un tagine avec un vendeur. Je crois qu'ils sont sur le point de l'acheter! Bien que ce ne soit pas très cher, ils devraient encore négocier. Moi, il faut que j'aille poster ma carte pour ma grand-mère. Avant de quitter Essaouira demain, je vais t'envoyer des photos. Je t'embrasse.

2. A g B i C d D c E b F a G h H f I e

3. Je viens de finir mes bagages et je suis sur le point de quitter Agadir. Avant de partir, il faut que j'aille dire au revoir à Nader, un jeune Marocain que j'ai rencontré à l'hôtel en jouant au tennis. Bien que je sois timide, je lui ai parlé. Après avoir joué au tennis tous les jours et après être allés à la plage ensemble, on est devenus amis. Je crois que je suis en train de tomber amoureuse! À bientôt!

Page 38

relative clauses using *qui, que, où, ce qui* or *ce que*	Les hôtels qui offrent un endroit où on peut se relaxer ce qui m'a choqué Ce que je préférerais, c'est
other subordinate clauses (using *quand*, etc.)	quand ils sont bruyants et sales quand nous lui en avons parlé
sentences using *si* (present/future; imperfect/conditional)	Si je pouvais, je n'irais plus à l'hôtel Si j'ai assez d'argent l'année prochaine, je ferai
direct object pronouns	Nous l'avions réservé je ne le recommanderai certainement pas ce qui m'a choqué
indirect object pronouns	quand nous lui en avons parlé
pronouns *y* and *en*	On y a trouvé des insectes quand nous lui en avons parlé
complex structures, e.g. verbal phrase + *de* + infinitive	Nous venons de faire l'expérience
en + present participle	En choisissant un hôtel
après être/avoir + past participle	après avoir lu
avant de + infinitive	avant de réserver
phrase + subjunctive	Bien que je ne sois pas exigeant

Page 40

Sample answer:

Salut !

En vacances, mes parents se relaxent et je les trouve plus cool, ce qui est agréable. Par contre, leurs sorties aux musées sont ennuyeuses!

On vient de passer des vacances catastrophiques. Après avoir fait un long voyage, nous sommes arrivés en Thaïlande. En allant à la piscine de l'hôtel, qui était horrible, ma mère est tombée et s'est cassé la jambe. Pendant qu'elle était à l'hôpital, mon frère était toujours en train de m'énerver et mon père ne lui disait rien. Bien que je sois patient, j'en avais marre! Après être sortie de l'hôpital, ma mère ne pouvait rien faire. On était sur le point de rentrer quand il y a eu un ouragan: les avions ne quittaient plus la Thaïlande, nous y sommes restés encore une semaine. L'horreur!

Si je pouvais, je passerais mes prochaines vacances avec mes copains. On irait camper au bord de la mer.

Unit 6

Page 42

1 i True:  c, d, f False: a, b, e, g

ii a Rubina thinks ~~learning a foreign language is more important than doing a school exchange~~. – school exchanges are a good idea when you are learning a foreign language

b She says there ~~aren't enough books~~ in the school library. – are books and also IT facilities.

e The European and African students worked together in spite of ~~language problems~~. – the distance

g They would ~~rather set up an exchange with a school in Pakistan rather than~~ with Louis Pasteur. – like to set up an exchange with a school in Pakistan as well as

2 a–b

En plus, le CDI, bien qu'il ne soit pas très grand, est équipé (non seulement) en livres, (mais) aussi en matériel informatique.

(Au lieu d')envoyer des mails individuels, comme nous le faisions auparavant, nous avons travaillé ensemble (malgré) la distance.

3 Student's own answer

Page 43

1 A *h* B *f* C *c* D *a* E *b* F *g* G *d* H *e*

2
- a (qui) était un mercredi,
- b (comme) Tom fait du judo après les cours,
- c (pour) donner des nouvelles
- d (ce que) j'ai apprécié bien plus que l'accrobranche.
- e (depuis que) je suis arrivé
- f (pendant que) Tom sortait mes bagages de la voiture
- g , (parce que) j'avais peur de tomber
- h , (qui) sont venus me chercher à la gare

3 Sample answers:

a Comme il y avait beaucoup de circulation sur l'autoroute, nous sommes arrivés à minuit.

b Je pense que les parents de Morgane sont vraiment très sympa.

c Leur maison, que je trouve petite mais qui est située au centre ville, est confortable.

d J'ai demandé le code wifi pour envoyer un message à mes parents.

e J'ai partagé la chambre de Morgane, puisqu'elle a deux sœurs qui dorment dans une autre chambre.

4 Student's own answer

Page 44

1

a Je déteste mon uniforme, **même si** le blazer est élégant.

b Le règlement du collège est strict et (d'ailleurs), les élèves protestent.

c Mon uniforme comprend un pantalon, une chemise, un blazer, (sans oublier) la cravate bleue.

d (Non seulement) les cours commencent tôt, (mais en plus) ils finissent tard, à 17 heures.

e L'été, **au lieu de** prendre le car, je vais au collège à vélo.

f (Grâce aux) grandes vacances, on peut bien se reposer l'été.

g J'ai cours tous les jours du lundi au samedi, **sauf** le mercredi après-midi.

h **Malgré** le règlement, beaucoup d'élèves ont des piercings.

i Si on a de mauvaises notes, il est fréquent de redoubler, (c'est-à-dire) de rester dans la même classe.

j On n'a pas le droit de quitter le collège **sans** permission.

2

Example or argument		Contrast or contradiction	
as it happens	(et) d'ailleurs	instead of	au lieu de
not forgetting	sans oublier	even if	même si
thanks to	grâce à	in spite of	malgré
not only … but also	non seulement … mais en plus	without	sans
that is to say	c'est-à-dire	except	sauf

3 Sample answers:

a Malgré de longues vacances scolaires, on travaille dur à l'école en France.

b Même s'il n'y a que 150 élèves dans mon collège, les équipements sont très modernes.

c Comme matières obligatoires, j'ai non seulement français, anglais, histoire-géo et SVT, mais aussi maths et physique. OR

Comme matières obligatoires, j'ai français, anglais, histoire-géo et SVT, sans oublier les maths et la physique.

d Quelquefois, au lieu d'aller en cours, on va à la cafétéria du centre commercial.

e Dans certains villages du Burkina Faso, grâce aux connexions Internet, on peut étudier à distance. OR

Dans certains villages du Burkina Faso, on peut étudier à distance grâce aux connexions Internet.

f J'aime les matières littéraires, c'est-à-dire le français, l'anglais, l'histoire et l'allemand. OR

J'aime le français, l'anglais, l'histoire et l'allemand, c'est-à-dire les matières littéraires.

Page 45

  1  5  3  2

2 Sample answers:

a 10 Les maths, ça va, mais je n'aime pas la physique et je déteste la chimie.

b 7 Le laboratoire de chimie est très ancien et il y fait froid l'hiver.

c 9 Pourtant, mon copain Pablo, qui est fort en maths, est toujours prêt à m'aider.

d 6 Comme je n'aime vraiment pas les matières scientifiques, je rate les cours et donc j'ai de mauvaises notes.

e 8 L'année prochaine, je vais certainement arrêter les sciences; par contre, je ferai un effort et je continuerai les maths.

3 Student's own answer

Page 46

1 (Non seulement) il faut arriver à l'heure, (mais) il est (aussi) interdit de manquer les cours sans raison, ce qui est normal, je pense.

En plus, on est obligés de laisser notre portable dans des casiers qui sont sécurisés grâce à un mot de passe.

L'année dernière, pendant «mufti», (c'est-à-dire) la journée où les élèves portent ce qu'ils veulent, la plupart des élèves étaient en jean.

Il y a une fille, (par contre), qui est venue déguisée en clown et (malgré) ses excuses, le directeur l'a renvoyée chez elle.

2 **Introducing an example:**

non seulement … mais … aussi

En plus grâce à c'est-à-dire

Introducing a contrast:

sans (x 2) par contre (x 2)

au lieu de malgré

3 Some of the phrases you could have copied are highlighted below:

different actions different places different time frames different people specific examples

Voici les règles principales. Non seulement il faut arriver à l'heure, mais il est aussi interdit de manquer les cours sans raison, ce qui est normal, je pense. En plus, on est obligés de laisser notre portable dans des casiers qui sont sécurisés grâce à un mot de passe. C'est important pour éviter les distractions en cours.

La règle la plus surprenante pour vous, ce sera probablement l'uniforme scolaire, que tous les élèves sans exception doivent porter. Par contre, les visiteurs comme vous peuvent venir en sweat bleu au lieu de l'uniforme complet.

L'année dernière, pendant «mufti», c'est-à-dire la journée où les élèves portent ce qu'ils veulent, la plupart des élèves étaient en jean. Il y a une fille, par contre, qui est venue déguisée en clown et malgré ses excuses, le directeur l'a renvoyée chez elle. À cause de cet incident, il n'y aura plus de journée «mufti» et le règlement va devenir plus strict. Nathan

4 Student's own answer

Page 48

Sample answer:

Bien que mon collège soit petit, il organise beaucoup d'activités extrascolaires. Cette année, par exemple, nous avons pu non seulement faire des rencontres sportives avec d'autres collèges, mais aussi visiter un château médiéval, assister à un ballet ou partir en randonnée au Portugal.

À mon avis, il est important de participer à ces sorties, même si on a beaucoup de travail. On découvre des horizons différents et en plus on se détend, ce qui est utile si on est stressé par les révisions et les examens.

Ma meilleure expérience cette année, c'était la visite du château médiéval. Il pleuvait un peu mais malgré le mauvais temps, j'ai exploré ces ruines et j'ai discuté avec un archéologue qui faisait des recherches.

Depuis que j'y suis allé(e), je m'intéresse beaucoup à l'histoire. D'ailleurs, quand j'irai au lycée, je m'inscrirai au club d'archéologie au lieu de faire du basket.

Unit 7

Page 50

1. she enjoys dealing with the public; she is hard-working; she is punctual; she is motivated; she speaks several languages; she has experience (work experience on a campsite)
2. a thinks b likes c liked d helps e will help f is not g is not
3. I believe – *je crois*
   I think – *je pense*
   I feel/I reckon – *j'estime*
   I am convinced – *je suis persuadé(e)*
   in my opinion – *à mon avis*
4. I enjoy – *j'apprécie*
   I am lucky enough to – *j'ai la chance de*
   What I really liked – *Ce qui m'a beaucoup plu*

Page 51

1. a P – formidable
   b N – Ce qui ne m'a pas plu
   c N – Je n'ai pas aimé
   d P – Le plus passionnant
   e P – J'ai adoré
   f N – J'ai trouvé difficile
   g N – Ça m'a beaucoup stressé de
   h P – Heureusement,
   i P – Je rêve de
2. a J'ai fait un stage horrible chez un vétérinaire.
   b Ce qui m'a plu pendant le stage, c'était faire le café.
   c J'ai bien aimé répondre au téléphone.
   d Le moins intéressant, c'était observer les vétérinaires.
   e J'ai détesté m'occuper des animaux dans l'infirmerie.
   f J'ai trouvé très facile de manipuler les animaux très malades.
   g Ça ne m'a pas dérangé de parler à leurs propriétaires.
   h Malheureusement, les infirmières étaient toujours là.
   i Je n'ai pas envie de faire un autre stage chez un véto.

Page 52

1. a–b
   A c – non seulement … mais de plus
   B a – comme/puisque
   C f – puisque/comme
   D b – En effet
   E d – grâce aux
   F e – par exemple … ou bien
2. Sample answers:
   a Selon moi, c'est essentiel parce que/car/en prenant une année sabbatique, on apprend à être autonome./Je pense que c'est essentiel. En effet, pendant cette année sabbatique, on apprendra à être autonome.
   b J'estime que/Pour moi, c'est une mauvaise idée: non seulement c'est cher mais de plus c'est une perte de temps.
   c Je crois que c'est très important puisque/comme/parce que c'est une expérience très enrichissante.
   d Moi, j'adorerais prendre une année sabbatique: par exemple, je ferais un grand voyage ou du bénévolat.
   e À mon avis, ce n'est pas bénéfique. En effet, j'estime qu'il est plus important de finir ses études.

Page 53

1. a–b
   Possible answers (many other combinations are also possible):
   1 J'aime bien mon job parce qu'il est intéressant et stimulant. Par contre, ce n'est pas bien payé.
   2 Je ne trouve pas mon petit boulot super puisqu'il est mal payé. Cependant, j'apprends beaucoup de choses sur le monde du travail.
   3 J'adore mon petit boulot. En effet, c'est une bonne expérience pour plus tard. En plus, j'apprécie mon patron qui est très sympa.
   4 Mon petit job me plaît assez, comme il est bien payé. Malheureusement, comme il n'y a rien à faire, je m'ennuie.
   5 Mon job est affreux: non seulement les horaires sont longs mais c'est aussi loin de chez moi. En plus, c'est très physique et très fatigant.
   6 Je déteste mon job car je m'ennuie beaucoup. Heureusement, je suis bien payé.

Page 53

2. Sample answers:

Opinion	Justification	Connective	Logical conclusion
a J'ai fait un stage fantastique	parce que le travail était intéressant.	Malheureusement,	c'était très fatigant.
b J'ai appris beaucoup de choses	non seulement sur le job mais aussi sur le monde du travail en général.	En plus,	j'ai gagné un peu d'argent!
c Je me suis passionné(e) pour le travail	car je voudrais faire ce métier plus tard.	Par contre,	les collègues n'étaient pas sympa.

Page 54

phrases introducing an opinion	je trouve, j'estime, mes parents pensent, selon eux, je crois
adjectives that imply an opinion	passionnant, important, excellente, (pas) utile, idéal
adverbs that imply an opinion	grâce à, malheureusement, contre
verbs that imply an opinion	j'ai adoré, j'aimerais, je m'intéresse beaucoup, j'adore
expressions of interest, likes and dislikes	Ce qui m'a plu le plus
suitable connectives to explain an opinion	car, puisque, parce que, en effet
suitable connectives to add a supporting argument	en plus
suitable connectives to introduce a contrast	mais, malheureusement

Page 56

Sample answer:

Mon métier idéal serait guide touristique. Je crois avoir les qualités nécessaires pour ça. En effet, je suis sociable et j'ai une excellente mémoire. En plus, il faut être fort en langues et en histoire-géo et je m'intéresse beaucoup à ces matières au collège.

Après avoir fini mes études, j'ai très envie de faire un grand voyage en Asie avec une copine parce que les voyages me passionnent. Avant de partir, je trouverai un petit boulot pour gagner de l'argent.

J'estime qu'une année sabbatique permet non seulement de se relaxer après le stress des études mais c'est aussi une expérience très enrichissante car on découvre des choses nouvelles. Par contre, voyager coûte très cher.

Selon moi, la famille, c'est essentiel. En effet, j'ai l'intention de me marier quand j'aurai un bon travail et je rêve d'avoir une grande famille, avec quatre enfants. Malheureusement, ce sera difficile si je voyage beaucoup.

Unit 8

Page 58

1
- a rising sea levels / dirty seas
- b try to limit their use of plastic / throw away plastic
- c think plastic is food
- d people her age
- e help clean the beach / collect litter
- f pay the volunteers
- g put up information signs

2
- a cela **nous** concerne tous
- b Je pense aussi **que** la pollution des océans, c'est scandaleux
- c des efforts **pour ne pas utiliser** de plastique
- d c'est notre génération qui va **en** souffrir
- e j'**y** vais souvent
- f la déchèterie **nous** a donné des sacs
- g la déchèterie **nous les** a rachetées (nous = indirect object prounoun; les = direct object pronoun)

1 *que* to introduce an opinion: b
2 direct object pronoun (DOP): a
3 indirect object pronoun (IOP): f
4 DOP and IOP used together: g
5 pronoun *en*: d
6 pronoun *y*: e
7 adverb after the verb: b, e
8 *pour* + negative infinitive: c

Page 59

1
- a I'm convinced (that) the government is going to reduce gas emissions. O
- b The car (that) my father has chosen is economical. R
- c The appliances (that) we buy use less electricity. R
- d I think we can generate less rubbish. O

2
- a Je suis certain(e) qu'on peut utiliser moins d'eau. O
- b Je suis sûr(e) que le verre est recyclable. O
- c Le bus que je prends est électrique. R
- d Je sais qu'il faudrait/on devrait prendre une douche. O
- e J'espère que tu as éteint l'ordi. O
- f Le papier que j'utilise est recyclé. R

3
- a faire plus **d'**efforts pour protéger l'environnement. +
- b acheter **des** produits locaux. Pl
- c boire rarement **de l'**eau minérale. U
- d consommer moins **d'**électricité. –
- e préparer **du** compost pour le jardin. U
- f installer **des** panneaux solaires. Pl

4 Student's own answer

Page 60

Tense ↓ Person →			*je/j'*	*il/elle/on/c'*	*nous*	*ils/elles*
Present	regular:	*-er*	espère			
		-ir	choisis			se nourrissent
		-re		dépend		
	irregular:		prends	est	sommes, détruisons	ont, sont
Imperfect			étais	avait	avions	étaient
Perfect	with *avoir*		ai vu, ai pris	a fermé		
	with *être*		suis allée	s'est caché		sont montés
Future			vais réfléchir, irai	restera		rouvriront
Conditional			voudrais	plairait	pourrions	préféreraient

2 a–b i suis allée – je = Érika

ii sont montés – ils = les orangs-outans

3 a Si j'étais riche, je **ferais** le tour du monde.

b L'été prochain, j'**aurai** 18 ans et je **travaillerai** dans un refuge.

c L'année dernière, une tempête **s'est produite** sur la côte et **a détruit** les maisons.

d Il y a 20 ans, la glace **a fondu** et les ours polaires **sont partis**. J'espère qu'ils **reviendront** un jour!

Page 61

1 i Les organisateurs d'Autremonde? Non, je ne les connais pas. (Pl)

ii J'ai un voisin âgé mais je ne l'ai jamais rencontré. (M)

iii Je n'ai rien dit à ma mère pour ne pas l'inquiéter. (F)

2 a Quand on m'a demandé d'aider les SDF, j'ai accepté.

b Nous avons écouté un conférencier qui nous a parlé de la pauvreté.

c Les chiens sont abandonnés et l'association va leur donner un refuge.

3 a J'aide au refuge pour animaux. J'**y** vais tous les samedis.

b La musique au festival est super. Les bénévoles aussi **en** profitent.

c Je connais un vieux monsieur dans ma rue. Je vais **lui** téléphoner ce soir.

d Les sans-abri voudraient un logement et un travail. Comme je **les** comprends!

e J'ai besoin de l'adresse de l'association. Ils vont **me l'**envoyer.

f Au collège, nous avons demandé des informations sur le changement climatique. On **nous en** a donné.

Page 62

1 a jouer à des jeux vidéo

b pour trouver des aliments

c les gens ont des provisions

d après le dîner

e je suis sûr que j'y retournerai

f je pense que le bénévolat est une bonne chose

2 Sample answers: there are other possibilities in the text:

a (je) suis

b (moi et les autres bénévoles) sommes allés

c (ce n')était (pas)

d (les bénévoles) se sont assis

e (ça m')a ému

f (j'y) retournerai

3 a ils sont prêts à nous en donner [nous = moi (Kamal) et les autres bénévoles; en = des provisions]

b on m'a prêté un tablier [Kamal]

c je ne l'ai pas regretté [le travail au Resto du cœur]

d nous les avons écoutés [les clients]

e j'y retournerai [le Resto du cœur]

f ça nous permet d'élargir nos horizons [les jeunes]

Page 64

Sample answer:

Bien que ma ville ne soit pas grande, elle organise tous les ans un festival de danse folklorique qui a beaucoup de succès parce que des groupes du monde entier y participent. Je suis sûr que c'est aussi grâce à la bonne infrastructure hôtelière que la ville a créée pour accueillir les visiteurs et les loger dans de bonnes conditions.

Les premières années, nous avions un problème avec les voitures parce que les rues de notre ville sont étroites et mal adaptées à la circulation.

Il était impossible de les élargir. On a donc estimé que des parkings à l'extérieur étaient la meilleure solution et la ville en a construit deux.

L'innovation l'année prochaine, ce sera les toilettes sèches, car d'autres festivals nous les ont recommandées. Si on pouvait, on en installerait une dizaine, mais nous allons commencer par cinq. La ville est convaincue que les visiteurs en seront très satisfaits.

Unit 9

Page 66

1

Correct translation	Comments
J'habite dans un petit village depuis 2010.	*(present tense with depuis)*
Il n'y a rien à faire ici pour les ados.	*(nouns have determiners in French)*
Quand je serai à l'université, j'habiterai à Londres.	*(use the future tense after quand)*
J'ai hâte!	*(word-for-word translation not possible – need to find equivalent phrase)*
Si je pouvais, j'étudierais la musique	*(conditional form of the verb, no need for voudrais / the determiner la is needed)*
comme je ne suis pas mauvaise	*(mais was in the wrong place / don't miss out negatives)*
dans cette matière	*(beware of false friends like sujet)*
mais mes parents pensent que	*(mais was in the wrong place / que can't be left out in French, even though not needed in English)*
je devrais travailler dans leur magasin de chaussures avec eux.	*(make sure you translate everything)*

Page 67

1. 17 key points

Last Christmas, / my parents invited the whole family. / It was fun / but also a bit tiring. / I helped my mother / to do the shopping / and the cooking. / I got lots of presents / and my favourite was a mobile phone. / Next Christmas, / we will go skiing / in France / with friends. / If I could, / I would stay at home / with my grandparents / because I don't like winter sports at all!

2. Noël dernier, mes parents ont invité toute la famille.

C'était amusant mais aussi un peu fatigant.

J'ai aidé ma mère à faire les courses et la cuisine.

J'ai eu beaucoup de cadeaux et mon préféré était un portable.

Noël prochain, nous irons faire du ski en France avec des amis.

Si je pouvais, je resterais à la maison avec mes grands-parents parce que je n'aime pas du tout les sports d'hiver!

3. 1 B, g 2 G, e 3 F, f 4 A, d 5 E, a 6 C, b 7 D, c

Page 68

1. a Mes parents pensent que je devrais aller à l'université.

b Le passe-temps que je préfère, c'est le football.

c J'aime regarder les films mais je n'ai jamais aimé les comédies.

d Il achète toujours une carte pour l'anniversaire de sa sœur ...

e ... mais il ne la lui donne jamais ~~donne~~ ~~à elle~~.

f Nous aimons seulement la musique française.

g Je vais à l'école à pied le lundi~~s~~

h De temps en temps, j'aime aller me promener.

i Ce que j'aime faire ~~dans~~ le soir, c'est lire.

j Mon frère vient d'arriver en Écosse.

2. Mon père a pris sa retraite le mois dernier. Il travaillait dans une banque mais il n'a jamais aimé son travail. Maintenant il espère qu'il pourra faire ce qu'il aime le mieux: il adore le yoga et le jardinage. Je viens de lui promettre que je l'aiderai souvent dans le jardin. J'aime planter des légumes même si je déteste les manger!

Page 69

1. a passé b marchait c Le voyage d me reposer
2. a je travaille b je travaillais c je travaillerais d je travaillais e je travaillerai f j'ai travaillé
3. a Jouer b En jouant c Je joue d J'aime jouer e Avant de jouer f Après avoir joué

g (no word needed in French) h pour i d' j à k j'aille (subjunctive)

Page 70

1. Je suis bénévole/volontaire depuis trois mois.

En allant dans la maison de retraite, j'aide à divertir les personnes âgées.

J'adore ça!

Je joue souvent du piano et je chante aussi mais les résidents n'aiment que/aiment seulement les chansons démodées!

Mes parents m'encouragent à avoir un petit boulot pour/de façon à gagner de l'argent.

Je le ferais si j'avais le temps.

Page 71

1. J'ai acheté un nouveau portable pour remplacer le vieux que j'ai perdu parce que j'ai besoin d'un téléphone pour les devoirs. Je ne l'aime pas beaucoup/Il ne me plaît pas vraiment.

Si je pouvais, j'achèterais un iPhone mais mes parents pensent que c'est beaucoup trop cher. On a/Nous avons des ordinateurs à la maison/chez nous comme ma mère les utilise pour le travail: elle est romancière/écrivain/elle écrit des livres/romans. Quand j'irai à l'université, j'étudierai la littérature. Mes parents espèrent vraiment que je pourrai devenir bibliothécaire.

Page 72

A Quand j'étais plus jeune, je fêtais/célébrais Noël avec mes grands-parents. Nous mangions de la dinde et des légumes et mon père faisait toujours une bûche/un gâteau au chocolat.

L'année dernière, mes parents ont décidé de passer les vacances de Noël en France, donc nous sommes tous allés à Paris. J'ai pensé que c'était une très bonne idée mais Noël prochain, j'ai l'intention de travailler dans un magasin pour gagner de l'argent que je dois avoir pour payer mes études. J'irai à l'université si je réussis mes examens.

B Je viens d'arriver à Londres. Avant de venir ici, j'habitais à la campagne. J'adorais/j'aimais beaucoup notre ancienne maison qui était petite et confortable et avait un immense jardin.

Maintenant, nous habitons/vivons dans un appartement que mes parents ont acheté récemment. Je dois partager/Il faut que je partage une chambre avec mon frère, ce que je déteste! Je préfèrerais vraiment avoir mon propre espace. Quand j'aurai des enfants, ils auront chacun une chambre/ils auront tous une chambre.